D&S
Vol. 17

Navy's
First Supersonic Fighter

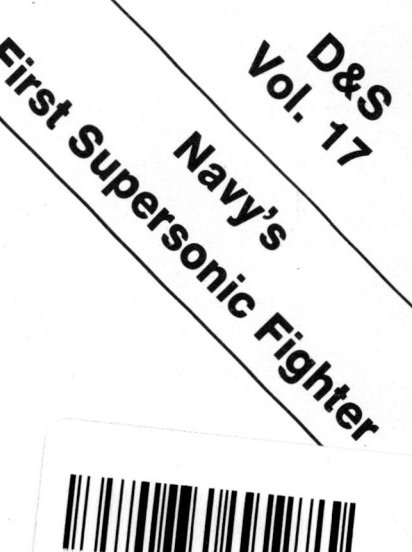

F11F
Tiger

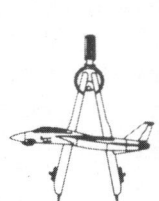 in detail & scale

Bert Kinzey

Aero Publishers, Inc.   U.S.A.

Arms and Armour Press   London - Melbourne

This book is a product of Detail & Scale, Inc., which has sole responsibility for its content and layout, except that all contributors are responsible for the security clearance and copyright release of all materials submitted. Published and distributed in the United States by Aero Publishers, Inc., and in London and Melbourne by Arms and Armour Press.

CONTRIBUTORS:

Ray Leader	The U.S. Navy
Lloyd Jones	National Archives
Al Lloyd	Ron Picciani

Grumman Aerospace Corp.

Detail & Scale, Inc. expresses a special thanks to Mr. H. J. "Shoney" Schonenberg and Lois Lovisolo of the Grumman History Center for their help and cooperation during the research for this publication. A special thanks is also due the Naval Aviation Museum for allowing the author special access to the cockpit and other details of the F11F that they have on display.

Most photos in this book are credited to their contributors. Photos with no credit indicated were taken by the author.

Printing 9 8 7 6 5 4 3 2

Published in United States by

Aero Publishers, Inc.
329 W. Aviation Road
Fallbrook, CA 92028
Printed in New Zealand

Published in Great Britain by

Arms and Armour Press
Lionel Leventahl Limited
2-6 Hampstead High Street
London NW3 1QQ
and in Australasia at
4-12 Tattersalls Lane
Melbourne, Victoria 3000
and in South Africa at
Sanso Centre
8 Adderley Street
P.O. Box 94
Cape Town 8000

Library of Congress Cataloging
in Publication Data

Kinzey, Bert.
F11F Tiger in Detail & Scale
(D & S; vol. 17)
1. Tiger (Jet Fighter Plane) I. Aero Publishers, Inc. II. Title: F11F Tiger in Detail and Scale.
UG1242.F5F13 1984 358.4'3 84-2947
ISBN 0-8168-5026-7

British Library Cataloging in
Publication Data

Published in the USA by Aero Publishers, Inc.

Front Cover: One of the F11Fs used in the ROHR testing is shown in this beautiful photograph. The leading and trailing edge flaps are lowered, and the landing gear is down, all making for an interesting in-flight shot.
(Grumman)

Rear Cover: Instrument panel in an F11F-1.

INTRODUCTION

This head-on view is of 138604, the first flying prototype. Note the wing fences and the long instrumentation probe on the nose. **(Grumman)**

With volumes on the F-14 Tomcat, F9F Panther, and F9F Cougar already in the Detail & Scale Series, only the F11F Tiger was left among Grumman's jet powered "cat" fighters that reached production status. The XF10F Jaguar did reach the flying prototype stage, but, having not reached production, and since there are no models of the Jaguar, that aircraft does not lend itself to treatment in the Detail & Scale Series. This book completes our detailed coverage of the Grumman jet fighters.

The Tiger was the least known of the Grumman "cats." Aviation writers have almost ignored the aircraft, and what has been written has usually been repetitive information on the Super Tiger or the use of the F11F by the Blue Angels. Some erroneous information has been published. For example, it has been written in a well known publication, released when the Tiger was in service, that all "long nose" Tigers were F11F-1F Super Tigers, equipped with the J-79 engine. In fact, only two "short nose" Tigers were tested as such. Almost nothing has been provided that shows the details of this, the first supersonic naval fighter. With the help of Grumman's super history center, Anacostia's photo files, the Naval Aviation Museum, and thorough research at the National Archives, this publication presents the most detailed look ever published on the Tiger.

By today's standards, the F11F was a relatively simple aircraft. There was no radar and no avionic bays full of "black boxes." Therefore, there are not as many details to cover, and this has allowed us to provide some coverage of the Tiger during operations at sea. These photographs show the Tiger during carrier qualifications and throughout its relatively short but colorful operational career. Additionally, we have been able to provide some coverage of the squadron markings that were used by units that operated the Tiger.

But as with all books in the Detail & Scale Series, the focus of this publication is on the details of the F11F Tiger. Cockpits are covered to include that in the mock-up and the experimental ROHR equipped aircraft. Landing gear, 20mm cannon, in-flight refueling receptacle, pylons, external stores, and other details are given extensive coverage. Attention is also given to the ROHR Tigers and Super Tigers, two variations to the basic F11F airframe that served completely different purposes. The ROHR thrust reverser was an experiment that explored the possibilities and capabilities of reversing thrust in flight. The Super Tiger was created by mating the F11F airframe with the J79 jet engine in the hopes of creating a more capable development of the aircraft.

Detail & Scale expresses a sincere thanks to "Schoney" Schonenberg and Lois Lovisolo of Grumman's History Center for their efforts and assistance during the research for this book. Through their cooperation, many never-before-released photographs were made available for this publication. Many were given to Detail & Scale on loan, and were "one-copy only" photographs in their files. They have contributed significantly to the coverage of the Tiger on the following pages.

DEVELOPMENTAL HISTORY

G-42039

This is Grumman's full scale mock-up for the Tiger design. At the time the aircraft was designated F9F-8. This was changed to F9F-9 when the -8 designation was given to the later Cougar series. Finally, the aircraft was designated F11F.   *(Grumman)*

The concept used in the development of what was to become the F11F Tiger was to optimize performance of the F9F-6 Cougar airframe. What was to actually materialize was an almost completely different aircraft. Grumman called the design G-98, and it originally was given the Navy designation F9F-8. However, this designation was later applied to the last of the Cougar series, which actually was a refinement of the original F9F-6/7 Cougar airframe. The Tiger designation then became F9F-9, and this was applied to the first three prototypes. At about the same time, the F10F designation was assigned to Grumman's variable swept wing design that became known as the Jaguar.

But design G-98 soon had more differences from the Cougar than it had similarities. It had a much thinner wing, fuselage-mounted intakes instead of intakes mounted in the wing roots, a low-mounted, all-flying tailplane, and an afterburning Wright J65 engine. The landing gear was moved from the wing to the fuselage, and full-span flaps were incorporated with spoilers. Ailerons were eliminated. The most notable new feature was the "area rule" fuselage. The idea behind this design feature was to lessen the cross-section of the fuselage where the wings were joined, by an amount of area that was equal to that added by the wings. This caused the area to be constant along the length of fuselage rather than becoming larger where the wings were attached. This would then cause less drag, and the airframe would become more efficient. The Tiger was the first aircraft designed from the outset with the "area rule" principle, and was the first flown with it.

With all of these changes, the F9F-9 designation

was not appropriate, and the Tiger was given the next available designator, that being F11F-1.

The aircraft was ordered on April 27, 1953, with both F9F-9 fighters and F9F-9P photographic reconnaissance aircraft being included in the contract. The first flight by the YF9F-9 took place on July 30, 1954, using a non-afterburning J65-W-7 engine. This engine was based on the British Sapphire powerplant. It was not until January 1955 that the aircraft was flown with the afterburner installed. At that time the F9F-9 designation was still used, but in April 1955 it was changed to F11F-1 as explained above.

The Tiger was intended to be a simple, lightweight, air superiority, day interceptor to protect the fleet. Like the F8F Bearcat, it was the smallest airframe possible designed around a given engine. The aircraft was so small that only the tips of the wings folded, and folding was accomplished manually. Fuel was carried in the thin main wing box, fuselage cells, and even in the vertical tail. Selection and transfer of fuel was automatic, and provisions were included for in-flight refueling. External fuel tanks could also be carried under the wings. As with the Cougar, internal armament consisted of four 20 mm cannon, but they were mounted in the sides of the intakes rather than in the nose.

The first flight without the afterburner was made by Corwin "Corky" Meyer from Bethpage, New York. Without the afterburner, the aircraft failed to go supersonic, but once it was installed. available thrust increased from 7,450 pounds to over 10,000 pounds, and level supersonic flight was easily achieved.

The Tiger soon made the headlines when, on September 21, 1956, Grumman test pilot Tom Attridge

MOCK-UP COCKPIT DETAILS

Instrument panel in the Tiger mock-up. (Grumman)

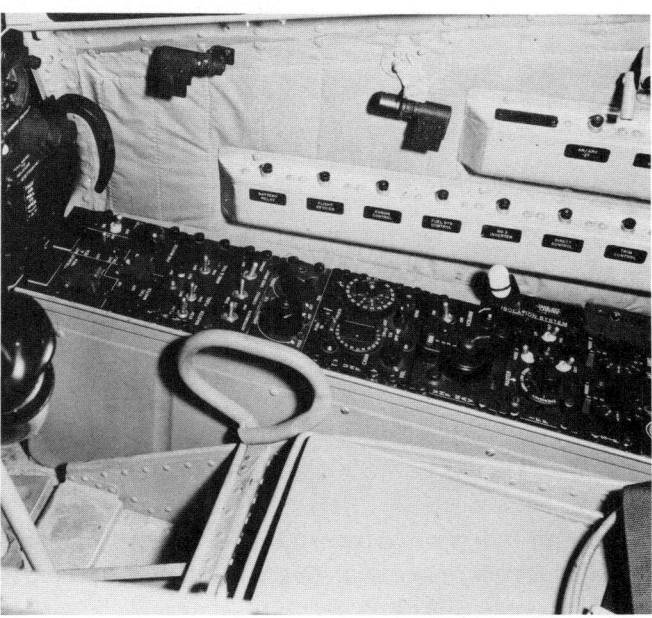

Right console detail in the mock-up aircraft.
(Grumman)

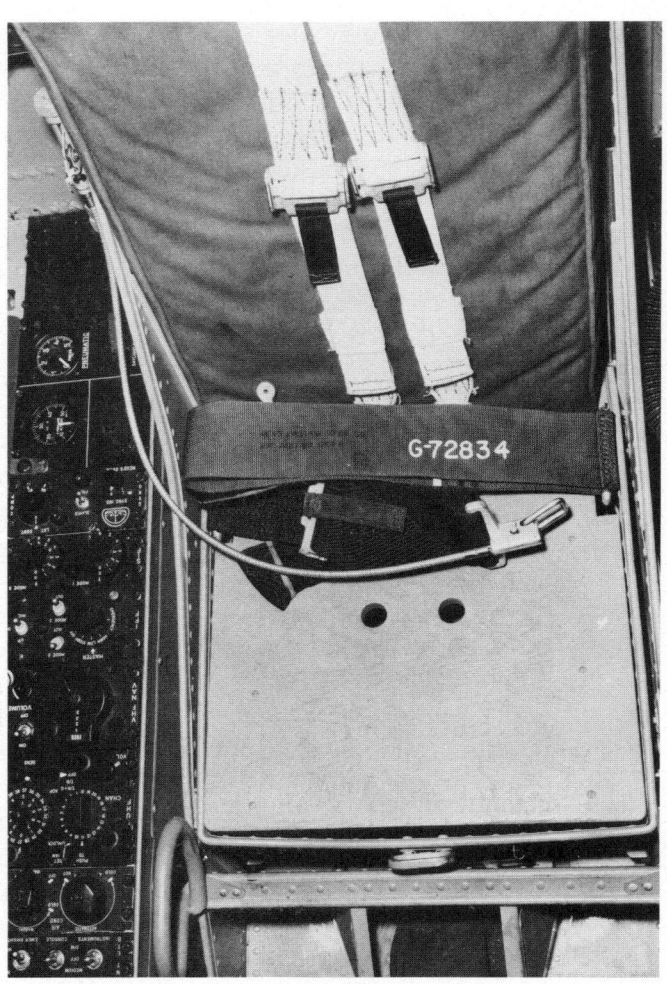

View looking down at the seat bucket. Note the shoulder harness straps, lap belt, and the details of the aft section of the right console. *(Grumman)*

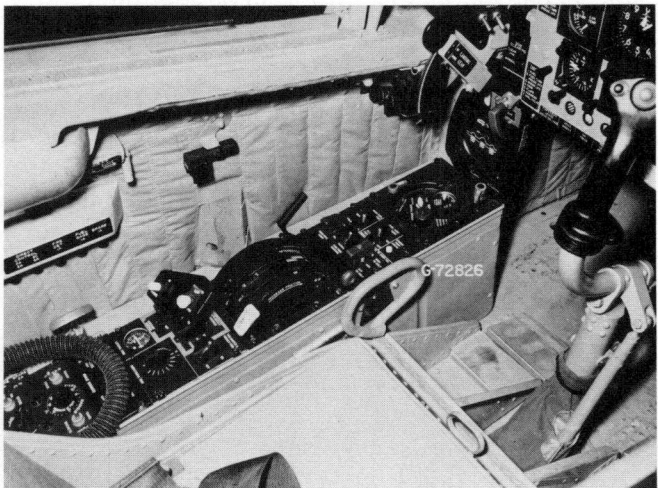

Forward section of the left console. *(Grumman)*

Aft section of the left console. Note the anti-g suit hose. *(Grumman)*

The first flying prototype, 138604, is seen here in flight. Note the lowered speed brakes under the nose and center fuselage section. The aircraft has no cannon or splitter plate ahead of the intake.

shot himself down by flying into shells that he had fired only moments before! The incident was used by the press to dramatize the speeds that the new jets were capable of attaining.

Carrier qualifications were conducted in April of 1956, and the Tiger entered service in March 1957. The last F11F was delivered in December 1958. At that time, Grumman's steady production of fighters for the Navy, that had been uninterrupted since the days of the F4F Wildcat, came to an end. It would be more than a decade before Grumman would again build fighters for the Navy. But in time, the production

Prototype, 138607, shows changes from 138604 seen above. A splitter plate is located ahead of the intake, cannon armament is present, and the nose is longer. See page 8 for more details. **(Grumman)**

line of fighters did reopen, producing the F-14 Tomcat.

The Tiger was produced in very few numbers, and it became the first Grumman fighter not to be delivered to the USMC. It certainly was not what could be considered a complete success, even though it gained a place in aviation history as being the first fighter with the "area rule" fuselage. It will also be remembered as the first supersonic aircraft in Navy service, and its use by the Blue Angels was also outstanding. Its design was excellent, but its lack of success and longevity of service can be blamed on its engine, which could not produce the performance of which the airframe was capable. The same problem plagued the F3H Demon. Further, with the F-8U Crusader entering the service with exceptional performance that greatly exceeded that of the Tiger, the F11F simply had nowhere to go. When possible foreign sales fell through, the production ended, and existing aircraft soon were removed from front line service and placed in training units. But it would be unfair to simply write off the aircraft as being unsuccessful. It was a step forward over the fighters that preceeded it, and it left its positive and lasting mark on aviation history. It was a sound and beautiful design, and it is unfortunate that it was not produced in larger numbers and that it did not serve for a longer time. It really deserved much better.

Production Tigers had a top speed of 752 mph at sea level and 890 mph at 40,000 feet. Rate of climb was 5,130 feet per minute, and the service ceiling was 41,900 feet. Fuel capacity was 1049 gallons, and a range of 1250 miles was possible with external tanks. Empty weight was 13,309 pounds for the "short nose" Tigers, and 13,428 pounds for the "long nose" version. Gross weight was 22,160 pounds.

PROTOTYPE 138604

This view of the first flying prototype shows many details to good effect. Originally the aircraft was painted overall gloss white. (Grumman)

From the rear, the exhaust pipe of the original non-afterburning engine can be seen. The housing for the tail hook and bumper skid is also visible.(Grumman)

Here, 138604 takes to the air for its first flight. (Grumman)

Escorted by an F9F-8 Cougar, 138604 has an uneventful maiden flight. (Grumman)

Here, 138604 is shown between flights as it receives attention from Grumman technicians. (Grumman)

PROTOTYPE 138607

A later prototype, 138607, shows several changes from 138604. Note the longer nose, intake plate, and cannon armament.
(Grumman)

The tail of the prototypes was more narrow in chord than that on production aircraft.
(Grumman)

This view shows the shape of the intakes and one of the two auxiliary intakes above the engine on the fuselage.
(Grumman)

From above, the leading edge wing slats can be seen in the forward position.
(Grumman)

The Tiger flies with other carrier-based aircraft of the mid-1950s. From left to right are the YA-4 Skyhawk, F11F Tiger, FJ-2 Fury, F4D Skyray, F3H Demon, and A3D Skywarrior. (National Archives)

Prototype, 138606, is seen here with the intake plate and 20 mm cannon. (Grumman)

This aircraft shows all of the developments included in the first "short nose" production batch except that an instrumentation probe replaces the standard in-flight refueling connector. (Grumman)

Missile armament was planned for the Tiger from the beginning. Here an early test aircraft flies with four Sidewinders beneath its wings. (Grumman)

TIGERS THAT NEVER PROWLED

An F9F-9P (later F11F-1P) was proposed with a nose similar to that used on the F9F-8P Cougar. The proposal was cancelled before any prototypes were built. (Grumman)

Grumman proposed a Super Tiger with the General Electric J79 engine. Although two airframes were tested with the engine (see pages 47-51), the aircraft was never put into production. This artist's concept shows what the production Super Tiger might have looked like. Sidewinder missiles are carried under the fuselage in much the same way they could be carried on the F-104 Starfighter, and fuel tanks, like those carried on the A-4 Skyhawk, are carried under the wings. The Tiger had a small fuel capacity for the thirsty J79, and this, along with the availability of the F8U Crusader, eliminated the F11F-1F from production consideration.(Grumman)

SHORT NOSE TIGERS

The first production batch of F11Fs were known as "short nose" Tigers. It had an in-flight refueling connector on the nose.
(Grumman)

The three prototypes were followed by an initial production batch of 39 aircraft which later became known as "short nose" Tigers. The BuNos for this batch (including the prototypes) were 138604-138645. Although these aircraft had noses longer than originally designed, they were noticably shorter than the second production batch which would be called "long nose" Tigers.

The "short nose" Tigers had an in-flight refueling receptacle fixed at the tip of the nose. Unlike those on the Cougars that came before, this receptacle was mounted right on the nose instead of being located on an extended probe.

Initial deliveries began in March 1957 to VA-156, which performed the fighter role despite its attack designation. "Short nose" Tigers also served with NATC and VC-3 for a time, and were also flown by the Blue Angels. However, they were quickly replaced when "long nose" aircraft became available. Once removed from front line service, the "short nose" version served on with training squadrons for some time.

"Short nose" Tigers were flown by the Blue Angels, and provided the team with its first supersonic aircraft.
(U.S. Navy)

A "short nose" Tiger poses with other Grumman aircraft of its day. Clockwise from the Tiger are an F9F-8T Cougar, an F9F-8P Cougar, C-1 Trader, HU-16 Albatross, E-1 Tracer, and S2F Tracker. (Grumman)

SHORT NOSE COCKPIT

The instrument panel in the "short nose" F11F-1 shows only subtle differences from that in the mock-up as seen on page 5. *(Grumman)*

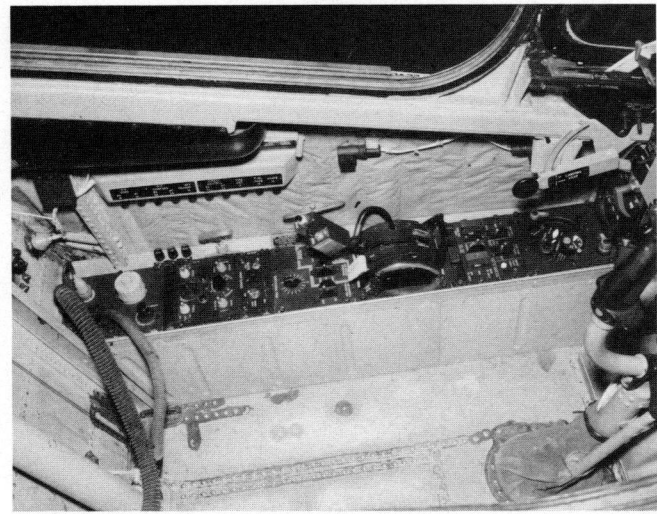

Left console and throttle quadrant. *(Grumman)*

Right console detail. *(Grumman)*

LONG NOSE TIGERS

The second and larger production batch of F11F-1s was known as "long nose" Tigers. The nose was lengthened in anticipation of the installation of a radar. The radar was never fitted. The in-flight refueling connector was replaced by a retractable probe as seen on page 23. This photo provides a comparison of the noses. The aircraft in the foreground, 138643, has the short nose, while 141797 is a long nose Tiger. (U.S. Navy)

Another change seen on the "long nose" Tiger was the addition of wing fillets at the leading edge of the wing root. This fillet is clearly visible just aft of the national insignia. (Grumman)

The second order was for 157 aircraft, BuNos 141728-141884. These were the "long nose" Tigers, and, in addition to the longer nose, they could be distinguished from the early production batch by a wing fillet located at the leading edge of the wing root. The longer nose had a radome fitted in anticipation of a radar being installed. To make room for the radar, the refueling receptacle was removed and replaced with a retractable probe located further back on the top right side of the nose. However, the radar was never fitted in the aircraft.

Long noses are evident in this line of Tigers, as is the black radome that was fitted but never used with a radar. (Grumman)

LONG NOSE COCKPIT

The instrument panel in the "long nose" aircraft showed several differences over the panel in the earlier aircraft. Compare this photo with that at the top of page 13. Color cockpit photos are on page 37 and the outside rear cover. *(Grumman)*

Left console detail. *(Grumman)*

Right console detail. *(Grumman)*

This photo shows another instrument panel configuration used in a "long nose" Tiger. The unusual control column is also shown to good advantage.

(U.S. Navy)

EJECTION SEAT

Courtesy of Grumman Aerospace Corp.

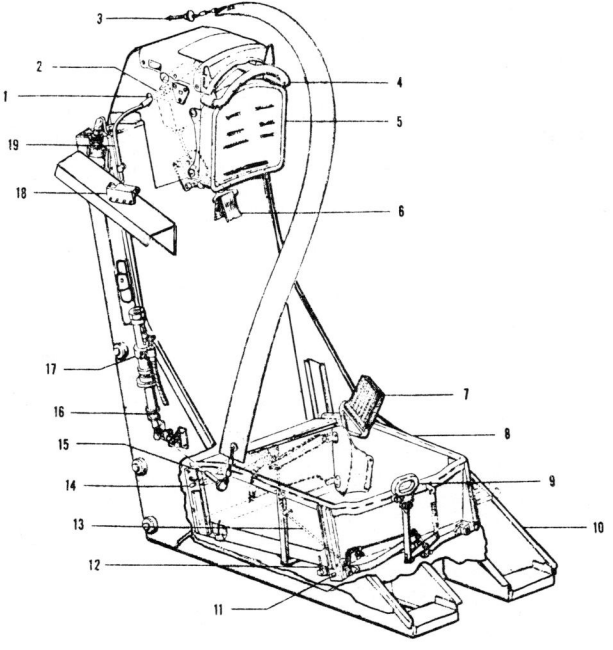

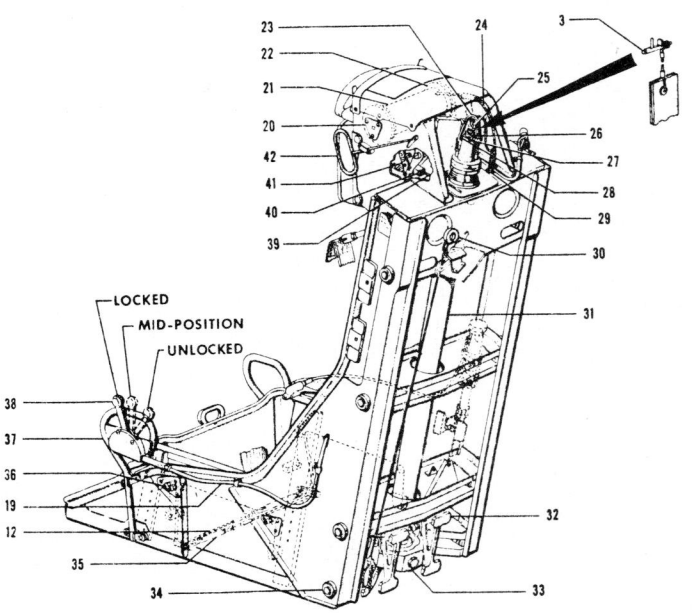

LOCKED
MID-POSITION
UNLOCKED

1. Firing Cable Inspection Hole
2. Shoulder Harness Inertia Reel
3. Ejection Seat Ground Safety Lock
4. Face Curtain Handle
5. Headrest
6. Shoulder Harness
7. Lap Belt

8. Seat Bucket
9. Bucket Height Control (Locking Pin Release)
10. Foot Rest
11. Height Adjustment Locking Pin
12. Bucket Counterbalance Cable
13. Locking Pin Control Cable

14. Height Adjustment Locking Pin
15. Automatic Lap Belt Actuator Ground Safety Lock
16. Sear Actuator
17. Automatic Lap Belt Actuator
18. Sear Actuator Striker
19. Inertia Reel Control Cable

20. Face Curtain Roller Bearing
21. Face Curtain Roller Spring
22. Face Curtain Roller
23. Firing Mechanism Yoke
24. Catapult Firing Cable
25. Firing Cable Disconnect
26. Safety Pin
27. Red Cartridge Indicating Band

28. White Line
29. Cable Spring
30. Seat Disconnect Ring
31. Catapult Tube
32. Bulkhead Seat Support Fitting
33. Catapult Support Fitting
34. Seat Roller
35. Bucket Counterbalance Spring
36. Counterbalance Pulley

37. Knee Brace
38. Harness Inertia Reel Control Handle
39. Canopy Jettison Control Cable
40. Canopy Jettison System Square Tube and Clamshell
41. Canopy Jettison Control Assembly
42. Ejection Seat Emergency Arming Handle

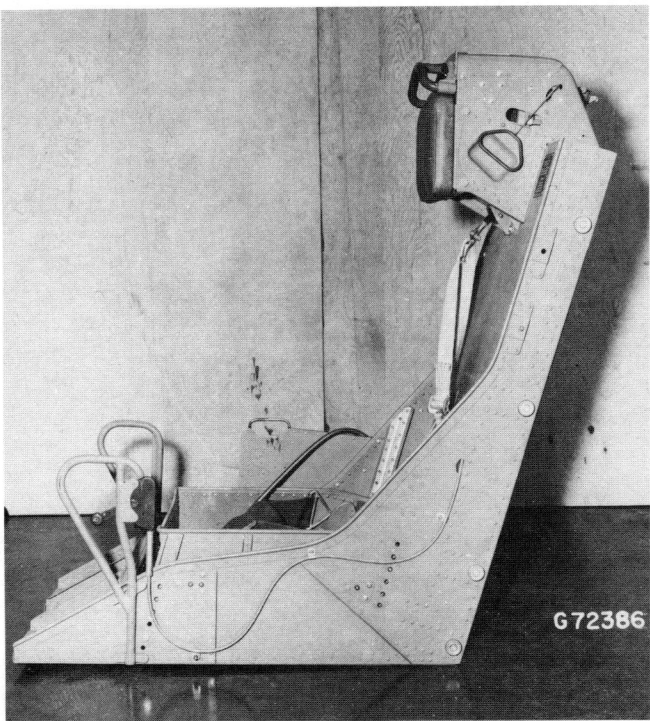

The ejection seat is seen here removed from the aircraft. (Grumman)

Ejection seat during testing. (Grumman)

20 MM CANNON

Right side guns as seen from directly in front. (Grumman)

Right side gun bay with guns in place. (Grumman)

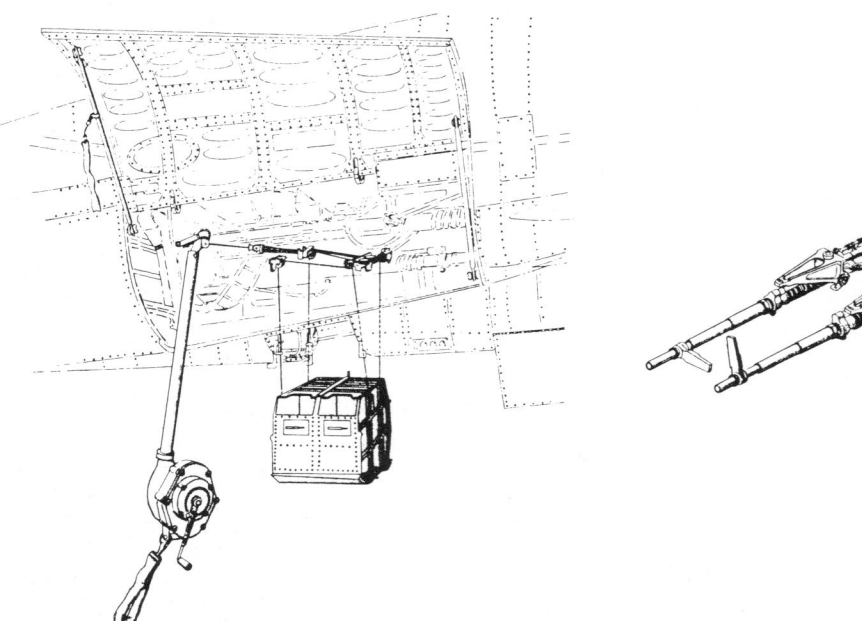

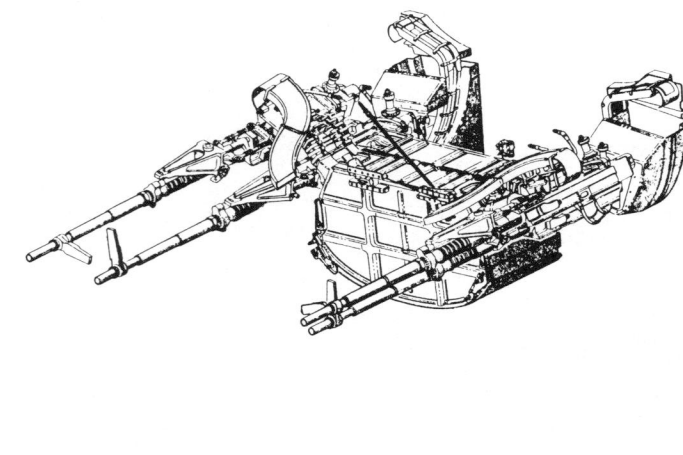

The ammunition box was hoisted by a special crank as seen here. (U.S. Navy)

This drawing shows the four guns with the ammunition box between them. (U.S. Navy)

Left side gun bay details. (Grumman)

Ordnance crew loading ammunition to the left side cannon. The ammunition box is resting on the ground under the aircraft.

(U.S. Navy)

SPEED BRAKES

Several speed brake designs were evaluated for the F11F before the production designs were decided upon. The production design for both front and rear speed brakes are shown in this view. *(Grumman)*

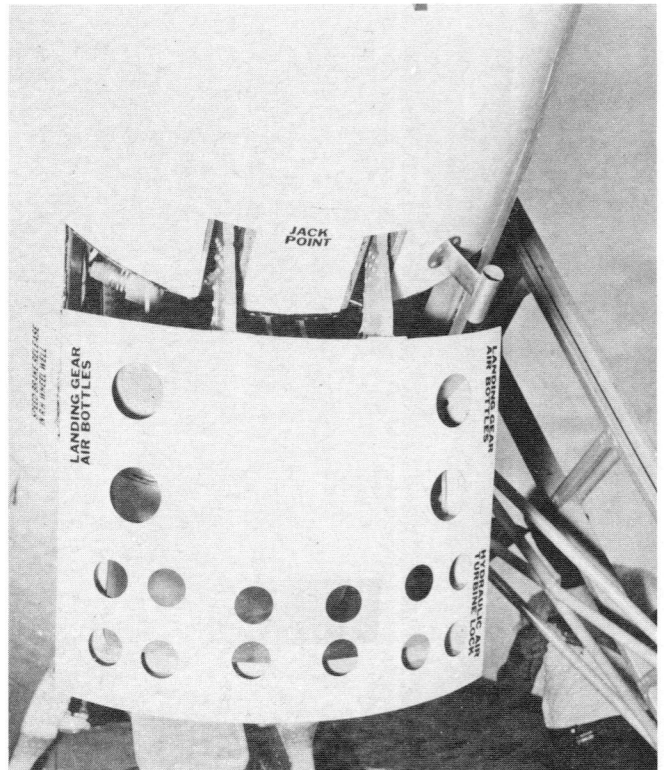

On flights 5 through 13, and 16, 138604 flew with a rectangular design with perforations. *(Grumman)*

A solid, generally rectangular design for the forward brake was tested on 138604 on flights 14 and 15. *(Grumman)*

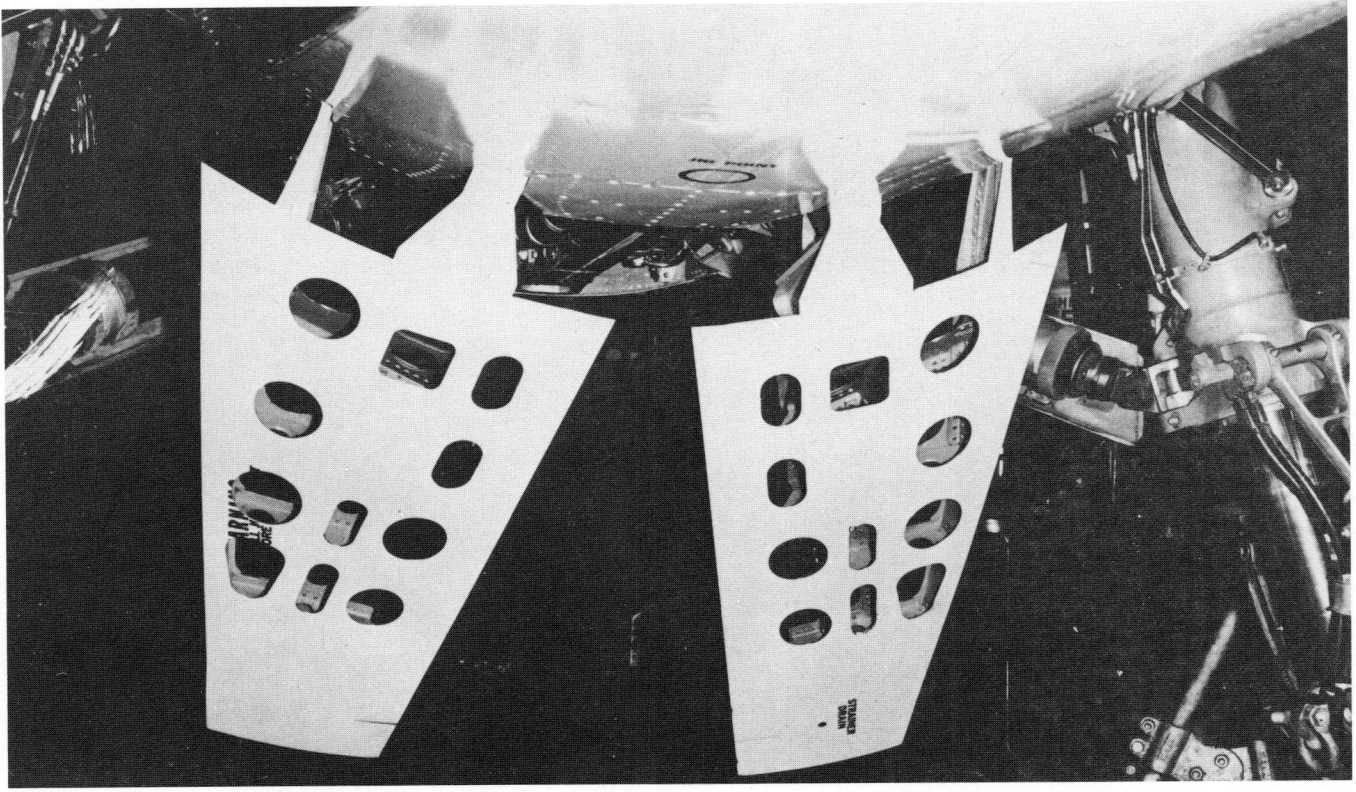

The final design for the front brake is seen in this photo. (Grumman)

The aft brakes were tested with perforations on flights 3 through 14 on 138604. The production brakes were of the same design, but had no perforations. (Grumman)

WING SLATS, FLAPS, & SPOILERS

The Tiger had leading edge slats and trailing edge flaps, shown here in the lowered position. The leading edge flaps were first used on the F9F Panther. They were also used on the F9F-6 and -7, but not the -8.

(National Archives)

The left leading edge slat is shown here in the forward or extended position. *(Grumman)*

The trailing edge flap is shown in the lowered position, and the spoiler is raised. *(Grumman)*

IN-FLIGHT REFUELING PROBE

The "long nose" Tigers had a retractable refueling probe on the top right side of the nose. Here, an F11F-1 refuels from an F-84F, while an F3H Demon waits its turn in the background.   (U.S. Navy)

In-flight refueling probe shown slightly open. This view shows the shape of both doors to good effect. The gun camera window is visible just ahead of the windscreen.   (Grumman)

Probe shown in the open position. The forward door closes once the probe has passed through.

(Grumman)

CATAPULT BRIDLE, HOLDBACK, TAIL HOOK & BUMPER SKID

Deck crewmen are shown attaching the catapult cables under the fuselage, while other crewmen attach the holdback under the tail. *(National Archives)*

This landing shot shows the tail hook in the extended position. The tail hook was hinged at the rear of the aircraft and folded forward. It was not of the sliding type as used on earlier Grumman fighters. *(U.S. Navy)*

Close-up of the catapult cable being attached under the aircraft. *(National Archives)*

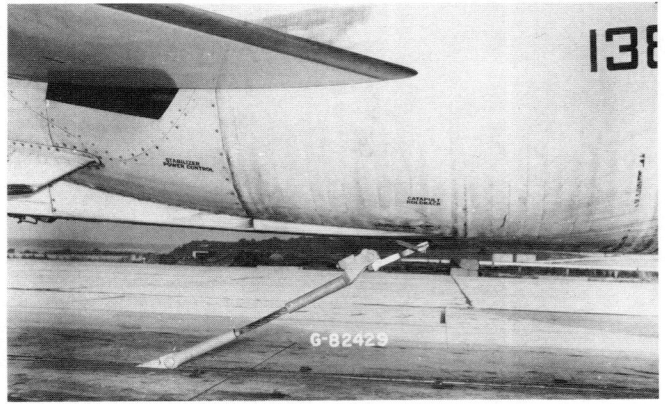

Catapult holdback detail under the tail section. *(Grumman)*

The cross section of the aft end of the fuselage is seen in this photo. The bottom was flattened to make room for the tail hook and bumper skid housing. *(U.S. Navy)*

LANDING GEAR

The landing gear detail of the Tiger is shown to good effect in this unusual photo. (Grumman)

Nose grear seen from the front right. A non-standard torque link, tried on one of the Super Tigers, is being used on this strut. (Grumman)

Head-on view of the nose landing gear. The details of the standard torque link with lightening holes are clearly visible here. (Grumman)

The left main landing gear is shown in this view. Note the design of the wheel and the strut arrangement. (Grumman)

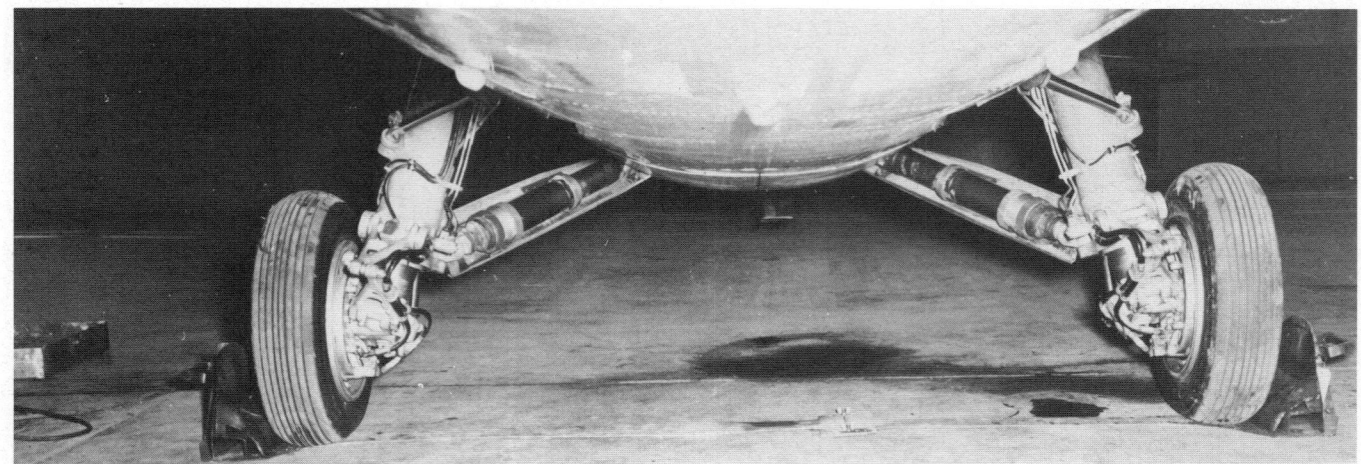

Retracting struts, brakes, and hydraulic lines are seen in this view of the main landing gear. (Grumman)

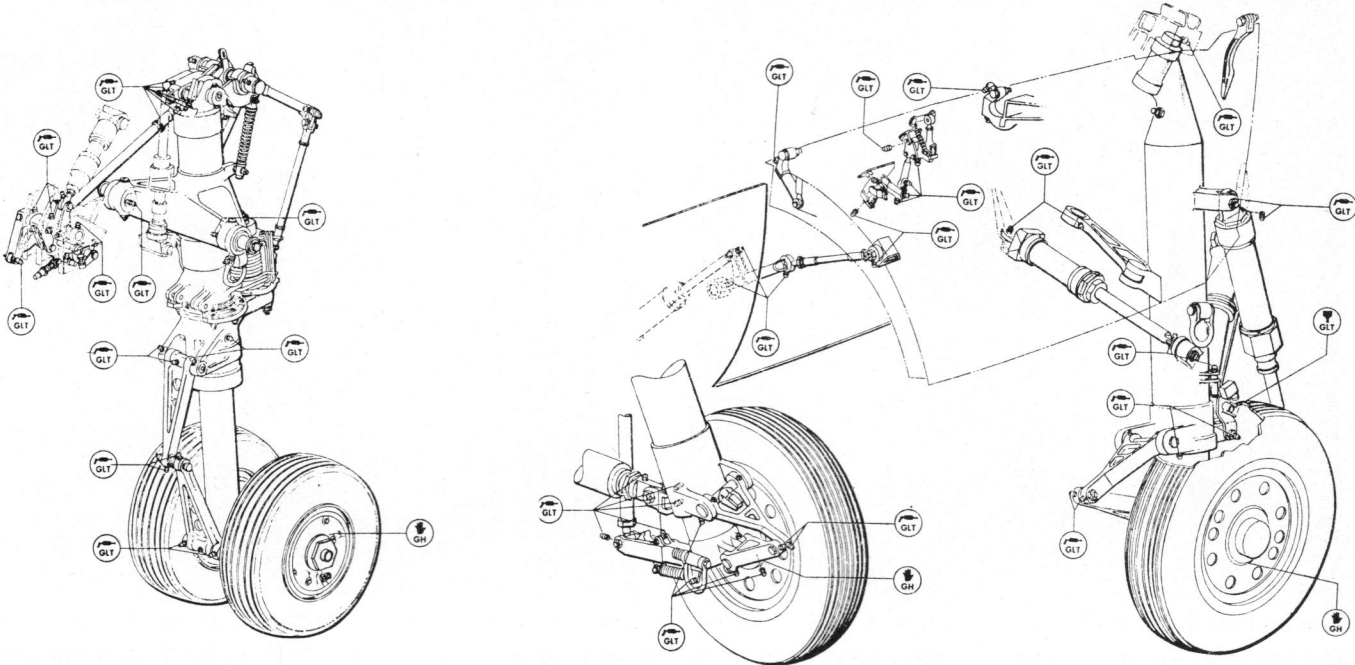

These two drawings, taken from the F11F-1 maintenance manual, show landing gear detail. (U.S. Navy)

View looking aft into the left main gear well. Note the actuating strut on the door. (Grumman)

Looking aft in the left main gear well. The right well was basically the reverse of the left. (Grumman)

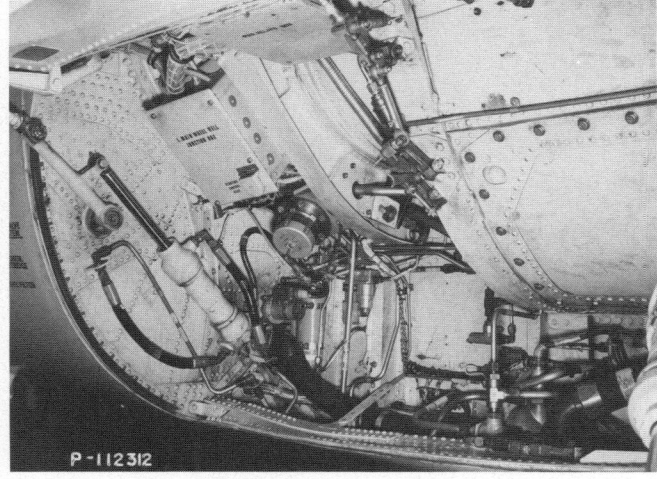

View looking forward in the left main gear well. (Grumman)

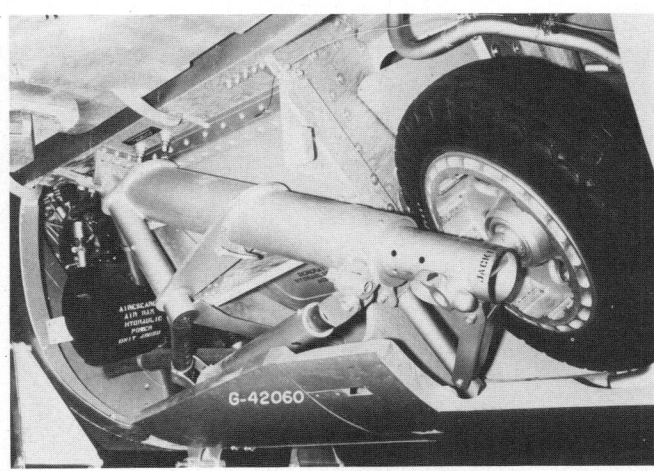

The design of the Tiger's landing gear was tested first in this mock-up. (Grumman)

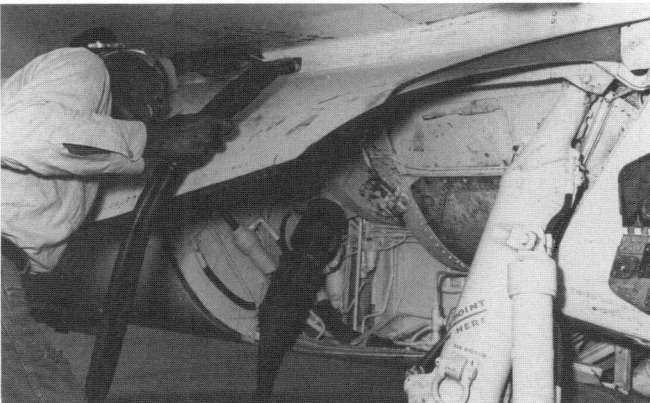

The compressed air hose, used for engine starting, is attached inside the left main gear well, while the electrical power is being hooked up just above the well. (U.S. Navy)

WING TIPS & HORIZONTAL STABILATORS

Only the tip of the wing folded manually on the Tiger. The wing fold joint of the right wing is shown in this photo.

Right wing tip detail with the tip in the extended or flying position.

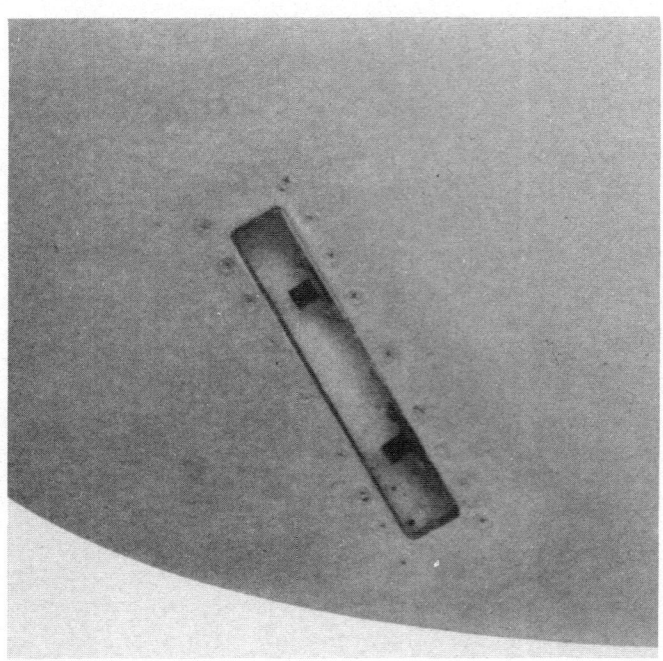

Small light on the wing tip on the right wing.

Light on the left wing tip near the trailing edge.

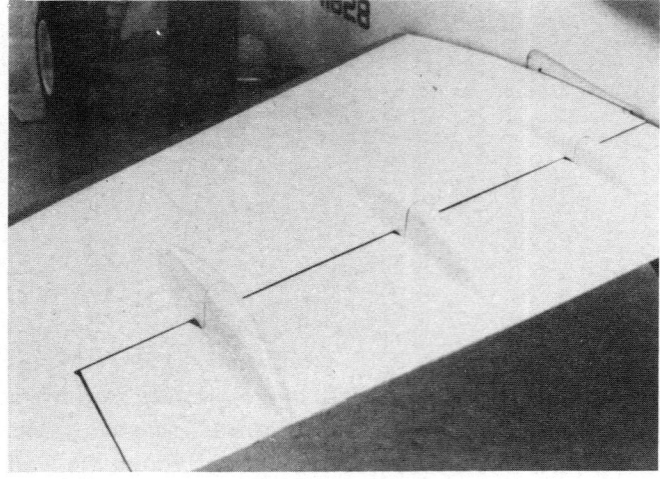

Left horizontal stabilator showing fairings.

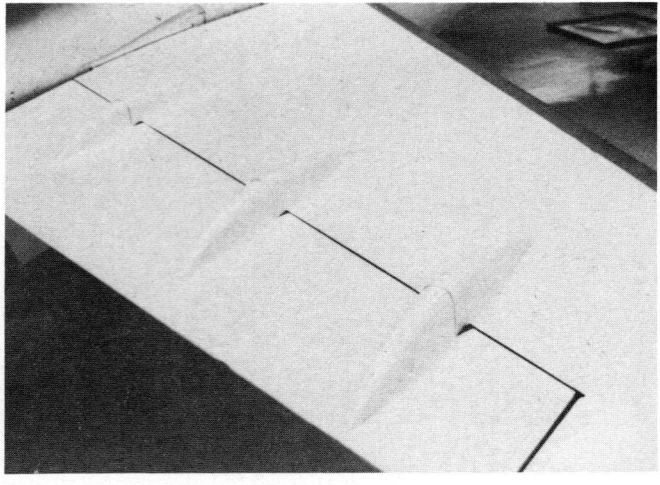

Top of right horizontal stabilator.

EXTERNAL STORES & PYLONS

The armament carried by the Tiger was limited by the aircraft's size and range. Fuel tanks, bombs, 2.75 inch rockets, and Sidewinder missiles were certified as external stores for the F11F. In practice, Tigers were seldom seen with external stores other than Sidewinders.

(Grumman)

BOMBS

A 500 pound bomb is carried on the inboard pylon with a Sidewinder on the outboard pylon. (Grumman)

Crewmen load a 750 pound bomb on the inboard pylon. (Grumman)

The detail of the outboard pylon is shown in this photo. A 500 pound bomb is attached. (Grumman)

ROCKETS & MISSILES

Four rocket pods of two different sizes arm this F11F. *(Grumman)*

Close-up of 2.75 inch rocket pods under the right wing. *(Grumman)*

The external store most often seen on the Tiger was the Sidewinder missile. They were carried in pairs or in fours.
(Grumman)

SYSTEM DESIGNS

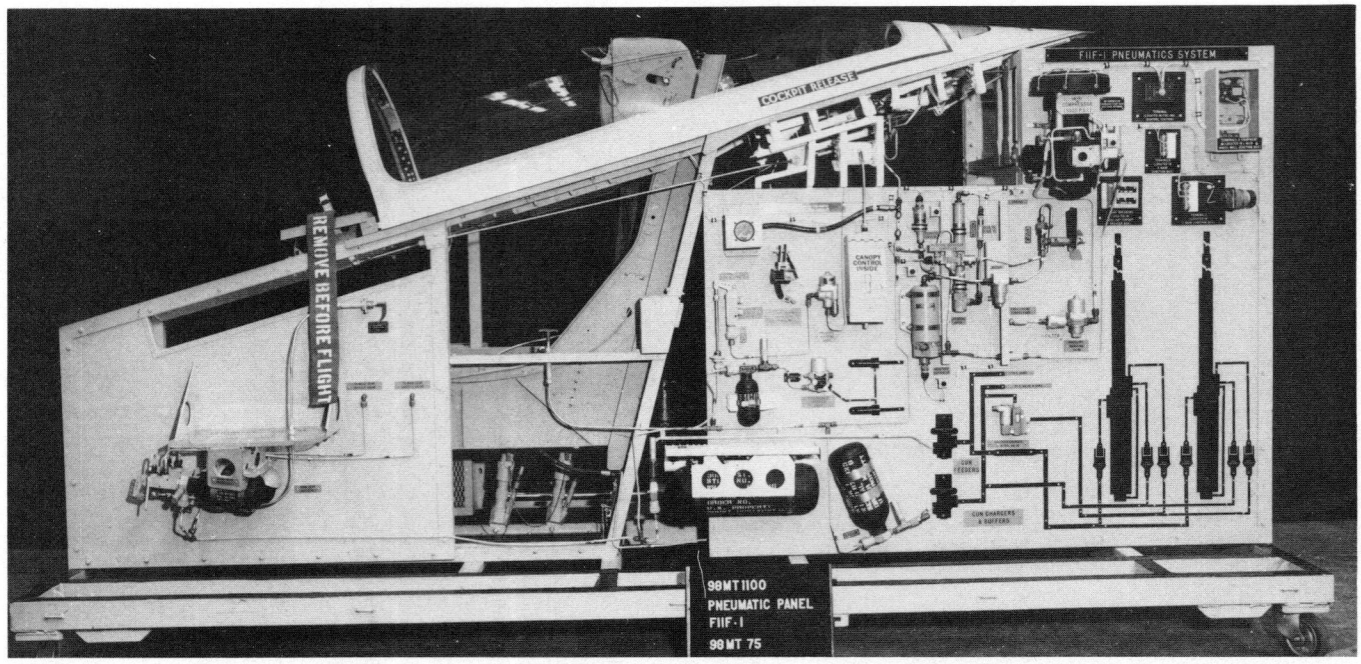

The photos on this page show several of the F11F's systems laid out on functioning panels. These could be used to teach each system's functioning. This is the pneumatic panel. (Grumman)

The nose landing gear and emergency generator are mounted on this stand. (Grumman)

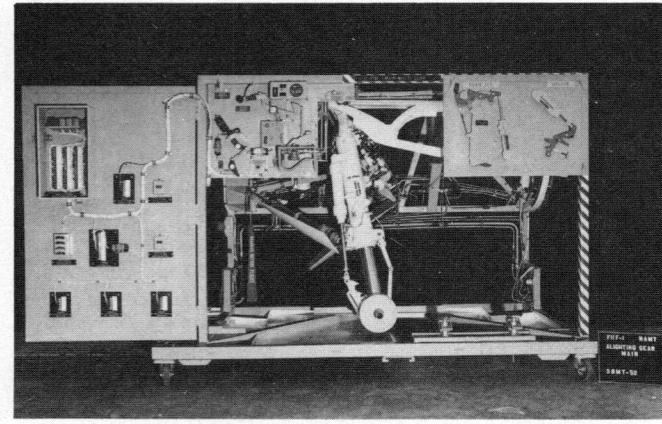

This panel shows the working of the main landing gear. (Grumman)

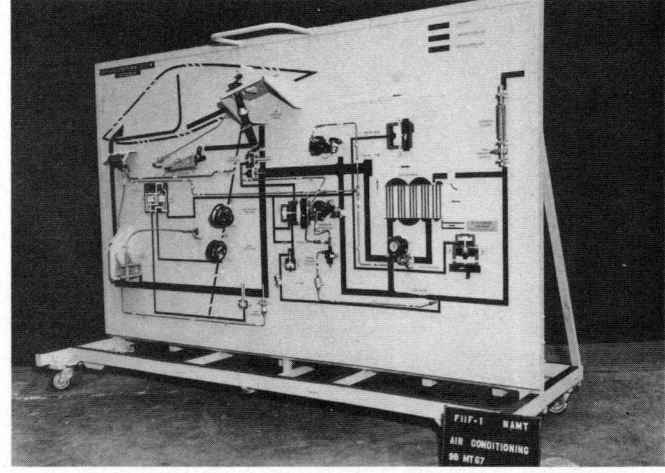

The air conditioning system is laid out almost like a schematic on this panel. The canopy has been painted on. (Grumman)

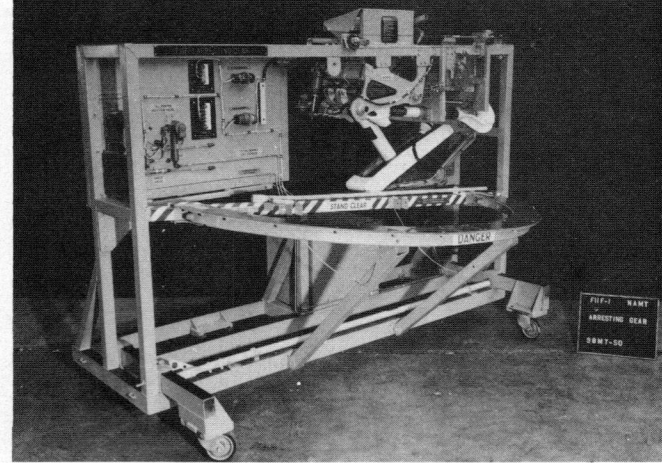

The arresting gear and tail bumper skid are shown on this stand. The tail hook is much shorter than the real thing. (Grumman)

TIGER COLORS

F11F, 138614, is shown in the markings of the Naval Air Test Center. "Test Pilot School" is written on the fuselage just above the leading edge of the wing.   (U.S. Navy)

Bright red markings have been applied to F11F, 138613. Note the open speed brake, open gun bay and gun loading door, and the folded wing.

(Picciani)

The same aircraft as shown above, 138614, is seen here earlier in its life on the USS Saratoga, CVA-60. It carries a Sidewinder missile and fuel tank under its wing.   (U.S. Navy)

THE BLUE ANGELS

Flying in their first short nose Tigers, the Blue Angels are seen passing Niagra Falls. (U.S. Navy)

This shot shows the long nose Tigers in the diamond formation with the lead aircraft inverted. (Picciani)

The leader's aircraft, 141828, is seen in this beautiful photo. Note the red under the lowered leading and trailing edge flaps. (Picciani)

Number 6 was 141738. The white wheel well for the right main landing gear can be seen in this photo. Wheel wells on Blue Angel Aircraft were white, but the inside of the doors and the wheels were blue. (Picciani)

Underside markings are clearly visible in this underside shot of all six Blue Angel Tigers. During the time the Angels flew the F11F, Number 7 was a two-seat F9F-8T Cougar. *(U.S. Navy)*

Trailing red and blue smoke. Number 4 shows upper surface colors and details to good effect. *(Picciani)*

This beautiful shot shows a Blue Angel F11F in-flight refueling from a KA-6 tanker. *(U.S. Navy)*

LONG NOSE TIGERS

Many details of the F11F are visible in this flying shot of a factory-fresh aircraft. **(Grumman)**

F11F, 141792, is seen here in the colors of VT-23 late in its operational life. **(U.S. Navy)**

F11F, 141783, was assigned to VF-33 when this photo was taken aboard the USS Intrepid in September 1959. **(Picciani)**

Tigers assigned to training squadrons usually had high visibility orange markings on the tail, wings, and nose, and a tail code consisting of a single digit followed by a single letter. **(Picciani)**

This NATC F11F, 141729, also has high visibility markings. The cockpit is receiving some photographic attention from an interested sailor. **(Picciani)**

COCKPIT COLORS

Instrument panel detail.

This view shows the unpacked ejection seat. Straps and headrest are visible.

Right console detail. The Tiger cockpit was characterized by very thin consoles.

Left console detail showing throttle. The unusual shape of the control column is also visible.

VF-21

Famous for their sharkmouth nose markings, VF-21 Tigers fly in a stacked formation. The last four digits of the BuNo is repeated on the tail. *(Grumman)*

The sharkmouth nose marking is clearly shown in this photo. *(U.S. Navy)*

Shown here is a line-up of several VF-21 aircraft. Note that the closest aircraft has red framework on the windscreen. In the background are several Furies and a lone Skyhawk. Under each Tiger is the ammunition box for the guns. *(U.S. Navy)*

SUPER TIGER COLORS

F11F-1F, 138646, is seen in red and white markings. The Grumman logo appears on the nose.   (Jones)

Super Tiger, 138647, is shown here in red and white markings with three stripes on the intakes.(Grumman)

At another point in time, 138647 carried these markings. Only one stripe is on each intake, and the red tail has been changed to white. General Electric publicity markings have been added above the BuNo. See pages 48 and 49 for more color schemes used on the Super Tigers.
                                                                                                                (Grumman)

ROHR TIGER COLORS

ROHR Tiger, 141853, is shown in flight without the thrust reverser installed. The Grumman logo is on the intake, and the tail markings are simple.
(Grumman)

Here, 141853, is seen with the thrust reverser installed. The Grumman logo has been added to the tail, as has the insignia for the Naval Air Test Center. Additionally, "ROHR" and "Inflight Thrust Control" has been added to the nose. A "Danger" marking is located on the fuselage ahead of the thrust reverser. Additional coverage of the ROHR aircraft begins on page 53.
(Leader)

DIMENSION DATA

DIMENSION	ACTUAL	1/72nd SCALE	1/48th SCALE	1/32nd SCALE
Length, "short nose"	529.50 in.	7.35 in.	11.03 in.	16.55 in.
Length, "long nose"	554.50 in.	7.70 in.	11.55 in.	17.33 in.
Wingspan, extended	379.50 in.	5.27 in.	7.91 in.	11.86 in.
Wingspan, folded	328.00 in.	4.56 in.	6.83 in.	10.25 in.
Height, top of tail	158.75 in.	2.20 in.	3.31 in.	4.96 in.
Tail span	182.00 in.	2.53 in.	3.79 in.	5.69 in.
Wheel tread	85.00 in.	1.18 in.	1.77 in.	2.66 in.

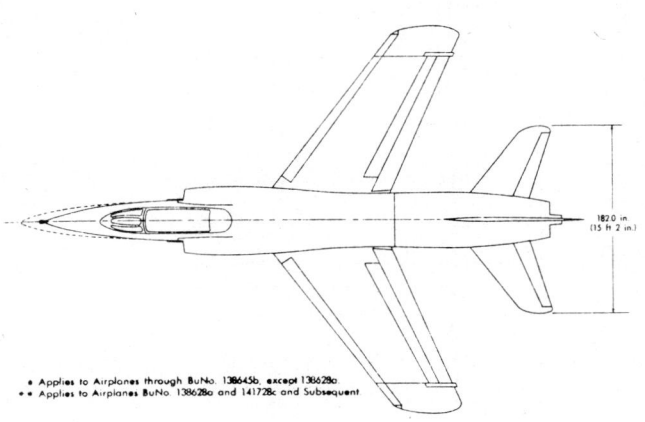

• Applies to Airplanes through BuNo. 138645b, except 138628a.
•• Applies to Airplanes BuNo. 138628a and 141728c and Subsequent

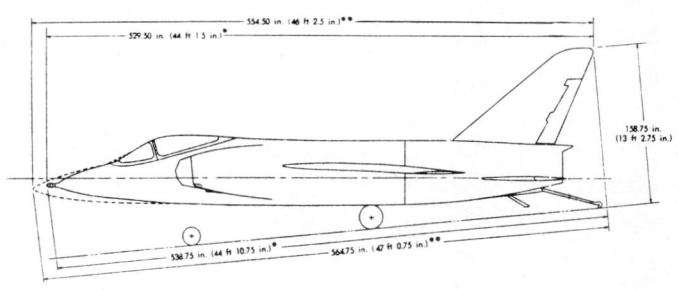

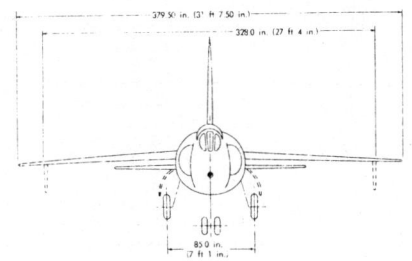

POWERPLANT

J65-W-18 Westinghouse with 10,500 pounds of thrust.

WEIGHTS

Takeoff: 21,237 Pounds, 6,663 Pounds Fuel
Combat: 18,572 Pounds, 3,998 Pounds Fuel
Landing: 15,907 Pounds, 1,333 Pounds Fuel

TECHNICAL DATA

WING

Section (Root): 65A006 MOD
Section (Tip): 65A004 MOD
Incidence-Root and Tip: 0
25% Chord Sweepback: 35 Degrees

WING AREAS
Total: 250 Square Feet
Flap (Slotted): 35.82 Square Feet
    Aft of Hinge: 29.16 Square Feet
Flapperon: 21.3 Square Feet
Slat: 16.8 Square Feet

ANGULAR MOVEMENT
Flap: 30 Degrees Down
Flapperon: 55 Degrees Up
Slat: 20 Degrees

HORIZONTAL TAIL

Root Chord 74.2 in. Airfoil 65A006
Tip Chord 29.7 in. Airfoil 65A004

HORIZONTAL TAIL AREAS

Elevator: 10.9 Square Feet
Stabilizer: 21.8 Square Feet

ANGULAR MOVEMENT

Elevator: +26 Degrees, -0 Degrees
Stabilizer: +5 Degrees, -18 Degrees

VERTICAL TAIL

Root Airfoil: NACA 16.005.625 (MOD)
Tip Airfoil: NACA 16.005.625 (MOD)

VERTICAL TAIL AREAS

Rudder: 6.10 Square Feet
Fin: 44.16 Square Feet

ANGULAR MOVEMENT

Rudder: 23 Degrees Left and Right

Data and Dimension Drawings Courtesy of Grumman Aerospace Corporation.

AIRCRAFT STATIONS

1/72nd SCALE DRAWINGS

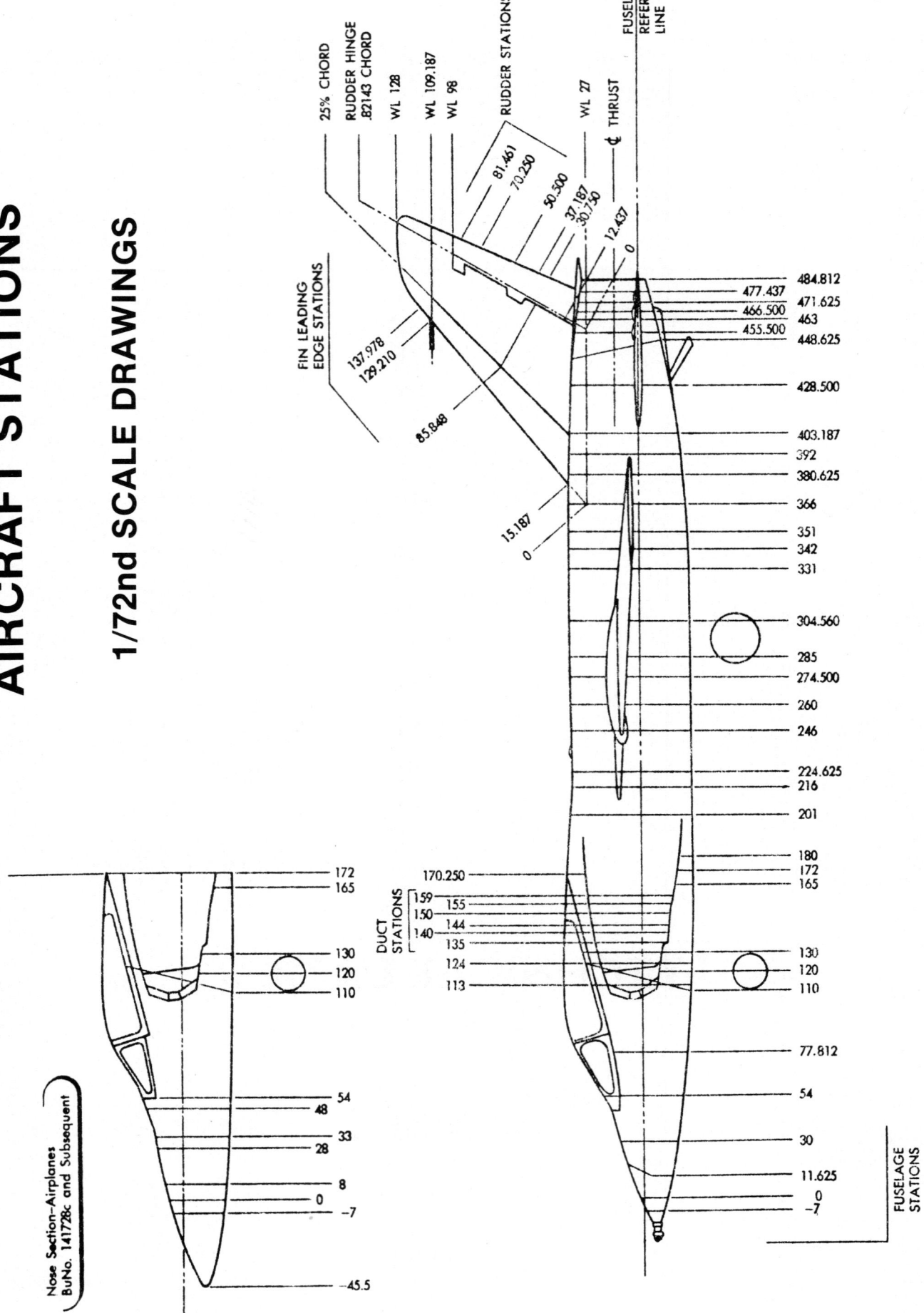

Courtesy of Grumman Aerospace Corp.

Nose Section–Airplanes
BuNo. 141728c and Subsequent

Nose Section–Airplanes
BuNo. 141728c and Subsequent

WING STATIONS

25% CHORD
FLAPERON HINGE
.70 CHORD

FLAP
STATIONS

STABILIZER
LEADING EDGE STATIONS

ELEVATOR
STATIONS

83
64
40

96
91
86
81
76
71.200
66.100
61
57.500
54
50.500
45.314
41
36.437
31

140
135.920
124.043

100

66.927

35

10.927

0 0

75

FLAP HINGE 92

FLAP HINGE 143

158.314

FOLD HINGE 161

189.890

163

FLAP HINGE 42

39

LEADING EDGE
STATION O
10% CHORD

39
42

44.314

18
20
24
28
34
39
49
53
58
65.187
68.125
74
85
92
100
107.156
115
124.875
133
135.920

80
89
95
110
118.625
128

102.781

BL 84.250
BL 91

25% CHORD

FLAPERON
STATIONS

10.5% CHORD

#6
#5
#4
#3
#2

#5
#4
#3
#2
#1

RIBS

64.093
69.062
97.750
107.188
122.818
141
150
163
177.688
189.313
198.858

66.901
89.500
105.062
118.437
132.625
148
156.500
173.315
187.188

WING SLAT
STATIONS

Courtesy of Grumman Aerospace Corp.

43

GRUMMAN F11F-1 TIGER

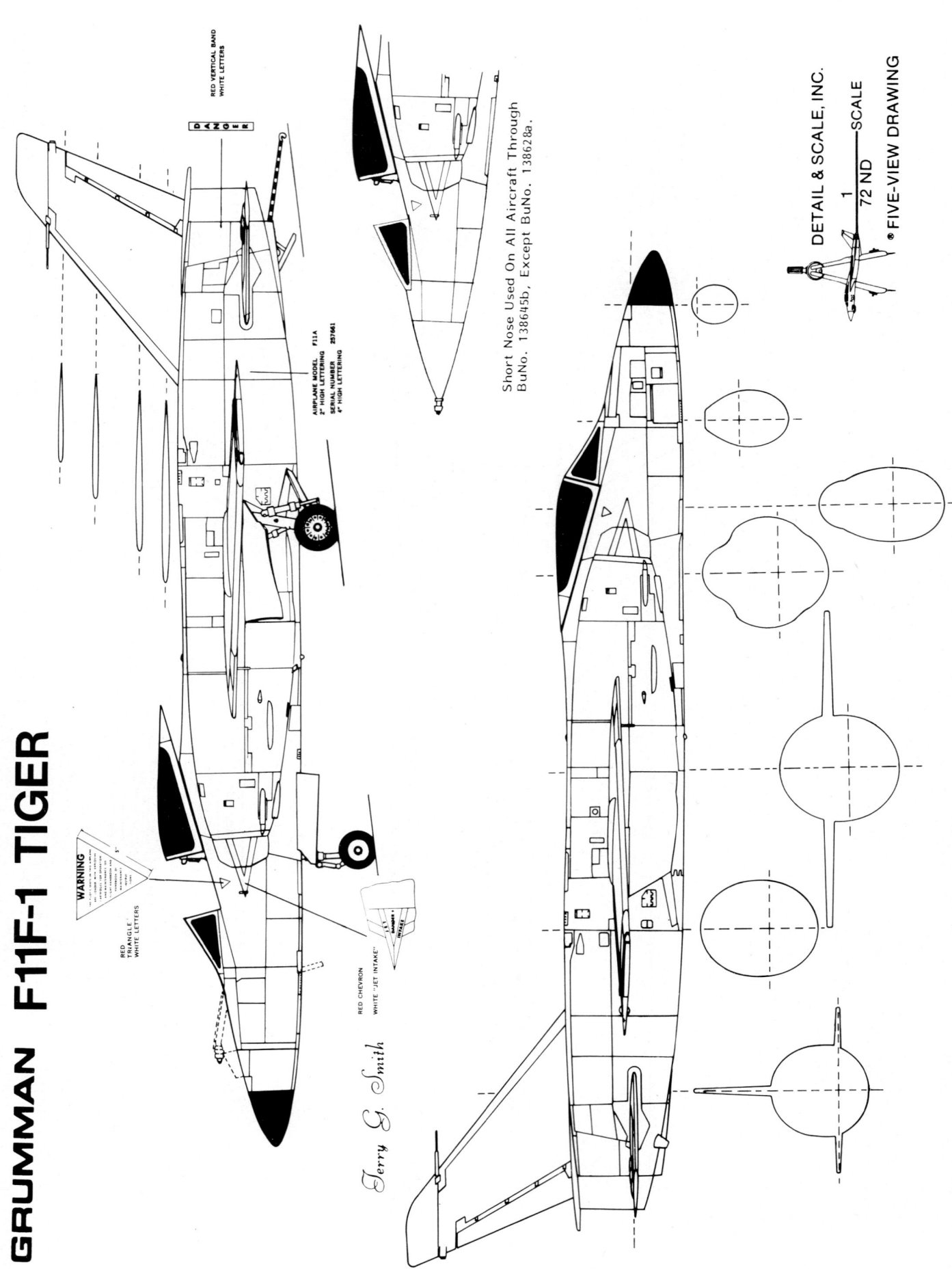

RED VERTICAL BAND
WHITE LETTERS

DANGER

AIRPLANE MODEL
2" HIGH LETTERING
F11A

SERIAL NUMBER
4" HIGH LETTERING
257661

WARNING

RED TRIANGLE
WHITE LETTERS

RED CHEVRON
WHITE "JET INTAKE"

Jerry G. Smith

Short Nose Used On All Aircraft Through
BuNo. 138645b, Except BuNo. 138628a.

DETAIL & SCALE, INC.

1
72 ND   SCALE

® FIVE-VIEW DRAWING

COLOR SCHEME

Non-specular light gull gray, 36440	All areas and surfaces visible from above except movable control surfaces
Gloss White, 17875	All areas and surfaces visible from below and upper surfaces of elevators, flaps, and flaperons. Both sides of rudder.
Black, 37038	All lettering and stripes on arresting hook.
Red, 11136	Jet intakes and outlet danger stripes.
Aluminum	All leading edges on wing and tail surfaces. Leading edges of jet intake.

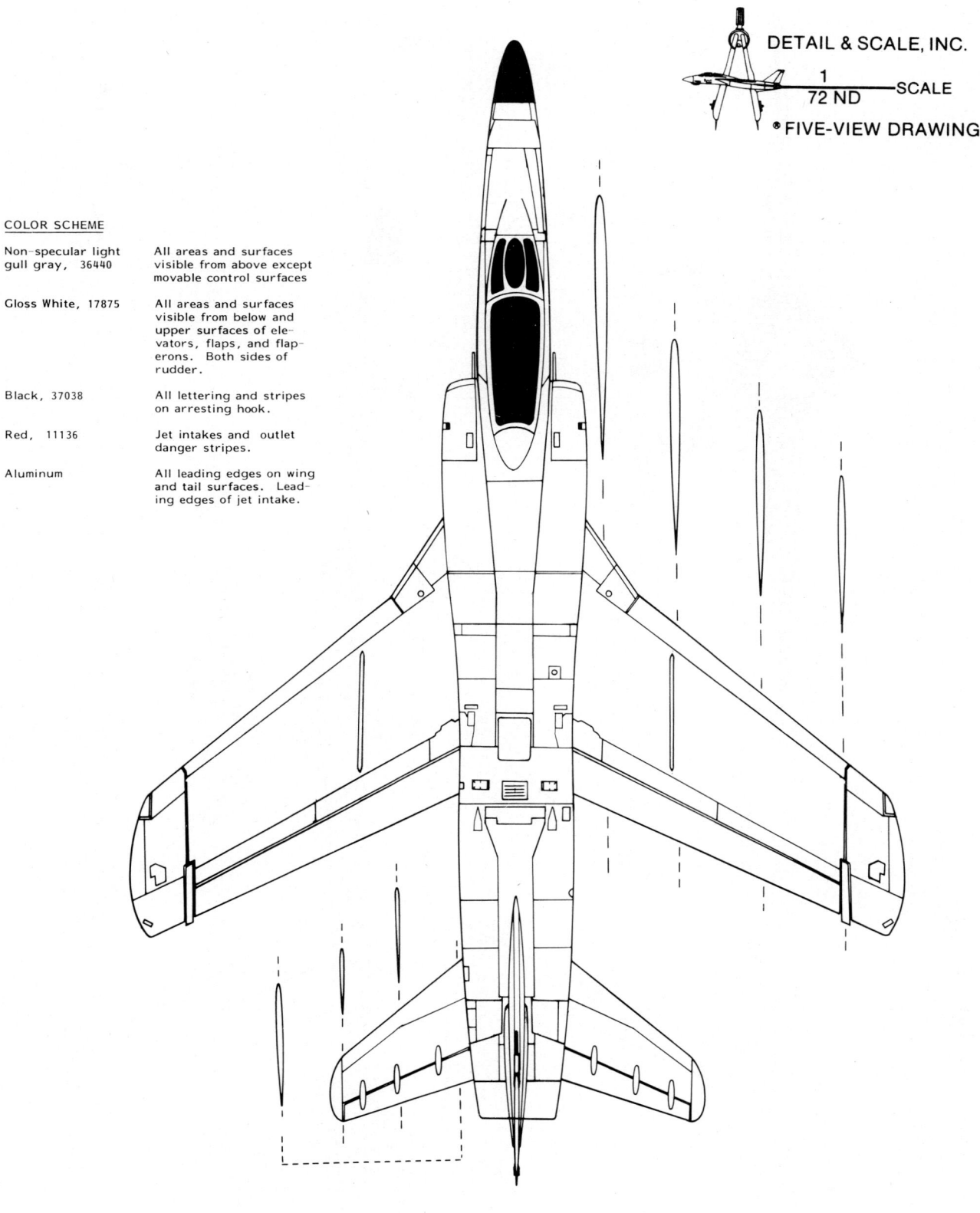

Terry G. Smith

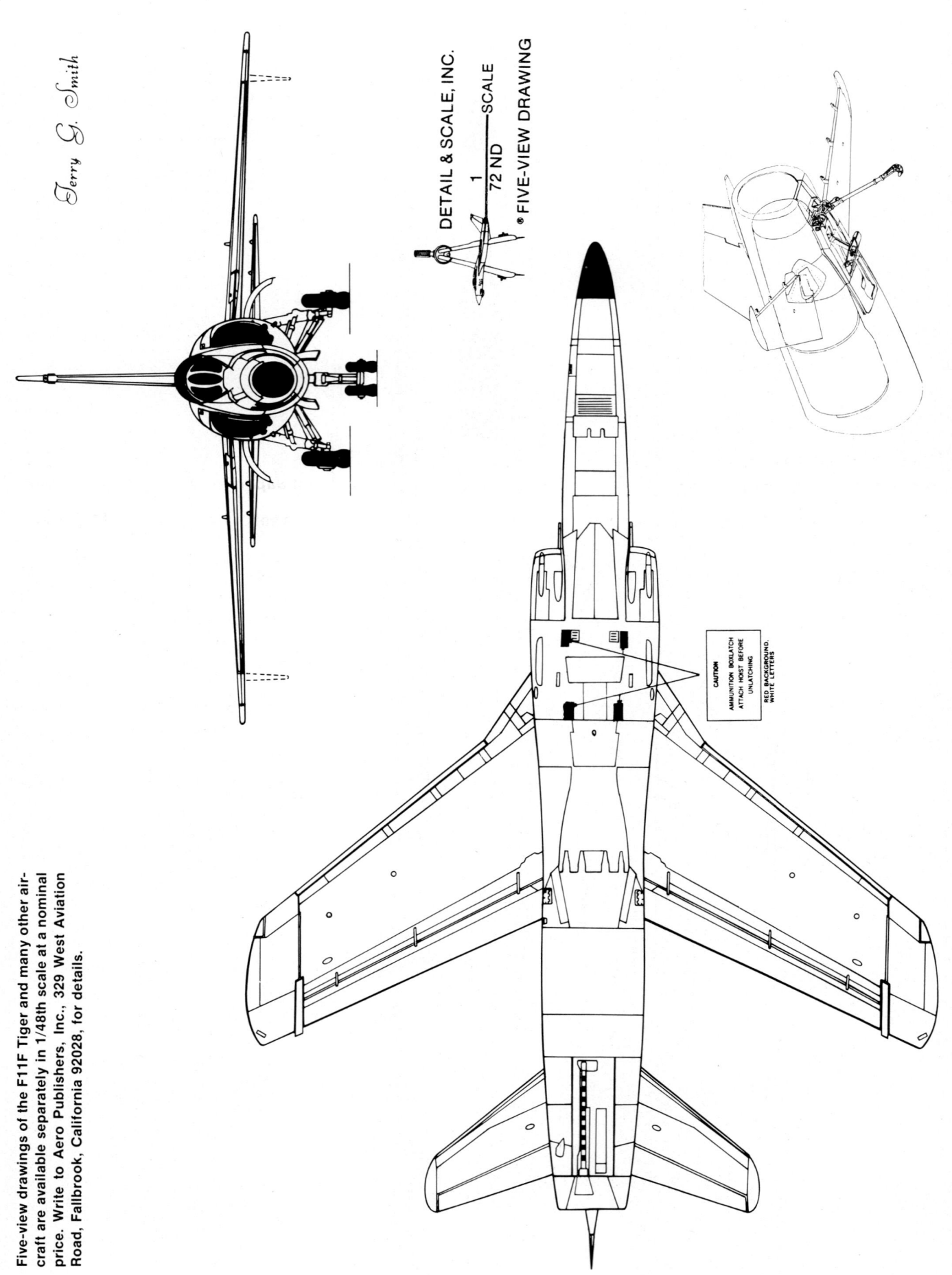

DETAIL & SCALE, INC.

1 / 72 ND SCALE

® FIVE-VIEW DRAWING

Jerry G. Smith

Five-view drawings of the F11F Tiger and many other aircraft are available separately in 1/48th scale at a nominal price. Write to Aero Publishers, Inc., 329 West Aviation Road, Fallbrook, California 92028, for details.

CAUTION
AMMUNITION BOXLATCH
ATTACH HOIST BEFORE
UNLATCHING
RED BACKGROUND,
WHITE LETTERS

F 11F-1F SUPER TIGERS

Two "short nose" Tigers, 138646 and 138647, were modified to the F11F-1F Super Tiger configuration with the General Electric J79-GE-3A engine. A longer nose was added in place of the original short nose. The Super Tiger set an unofficial speed record of 1,220 miles per hour and an altitude record of 76,939 feet. However, the engine was too big and heavy for the airframe, and a potential order from Japan fell through.   (Grumman)

Since the J65-W-18 left something to be desired in performance, Tiger orders fell one aircraft short of two-hundred, and this could hardly be considered successful or very profitable. Therefore, Grumman built two "Super Tigers" at their own expense in hopes of improving the performance to where it would be equal to or better than newer fighters that were soon to become operational. The J65 was replaced with a J79-GE-3A with 14,800 pounds of thrust in two test aircraft which were modified from two "short nose" Tigers.

As expected, the speed and climb performance increased dramatically. On April 13, 1958, test pilot LCDR G. C. Watkins set a speed record of 1,220 mph. On April 16, he climbed to 72,000 feet, then to 76,939 feet the following day. But, despite this excellent performance, the "Super Tiger" was not ordered into production. Designed around the smaller, lighter J65 engine, the wing simply could not adequately support the heavier J79. Additionally, fuel consumption of the J79 was great, and the fuel capacity of the Tiger was very limited. Thus the "Super Tiger" was short on endurance and range. So, while the "Super Tiger" was excellent for setting records, it lacked the all-around performance and maneuverability required to make it acceptable for production.

This rear view shows the enlarged exhaust area as compared to that seen on standard Tigers. The modification to the horizontal tail, most notably the lack of fairings as seen on page 28, is noteworthy.   (Grumman)

F11F-1F, 138646, is shown in this view. A long instrumentation probe was attached to the nose.(Grumman)

Underside details and markings of 138647 are seen in this view.　　　　　　　**(Grumman)**

Above: Left side view of 138647 in flight.
(Grumman)

Right: 138647 climbs at a steep angle during a test flight. *(Grumman)*

Below: A right side view of 138647 with slightly different markings than those seen in the photo above. A small portion of the General Electric marking on the tail is visible under the right wing tip. See page 39 for a color photo of the marking. *(Grumman)*

SUPER TIGER DETAILS

LCDR George C. Watkins enters the cockpit of one of the Super Tigers prior to a record altitude flight. Since the two F11F-1Fs were formerly "short nose" Tigers, some "body work" had to be done around the rear of the new nose. Note the instrumentation in the gun bay. Another noteworthy change that is visible in this photo is the new windscreen built right over the framework of the standard windscreen. *(U.S. Navy)*

A modification to the aft end of the canopy is visible in this view. The suit worn by LCDR Watkins during flights in the Super Tiger can be studied in this photo. *(U.S. Navy)*

The change to the intakes can be seen here. The shape has been changed, and the splitter plate has been removed. It has been replaced with a large number of small perforations in the fuselage skin just ahead of the intake. *(Grumman)*

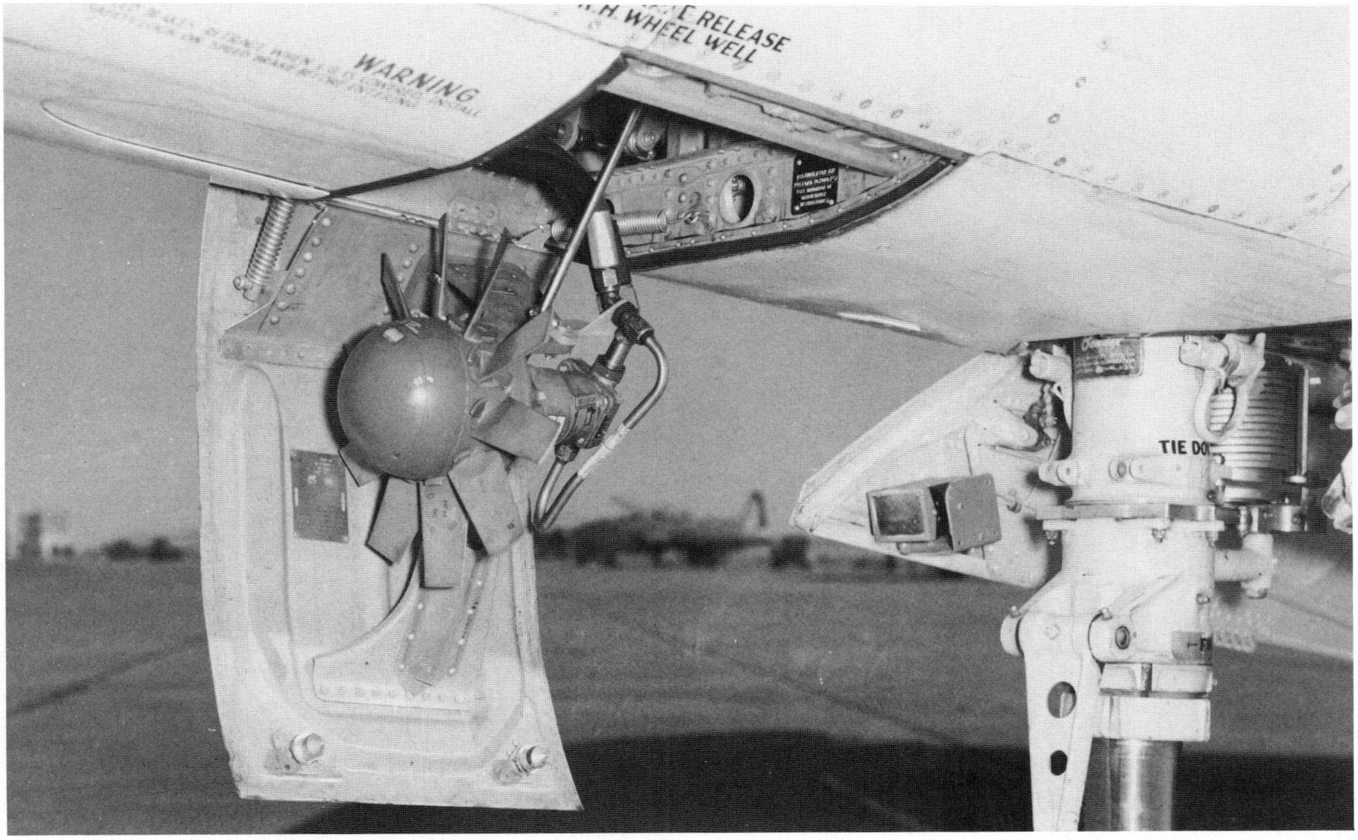

The ram air turbine for emergency hydraulic power is shown here, and is located just ahead of the nose gear. (Grumman)

The right intake, nose gear, and boarding ladder can be seen in this photograph. (Grumman)

This view is looking up into the massive tailpipe of the J79 engine. (Grumman)

At some point in time, ventral fins were tried on the F11F-1F. The shape of the right fin is shown in this view.
(Grumman)

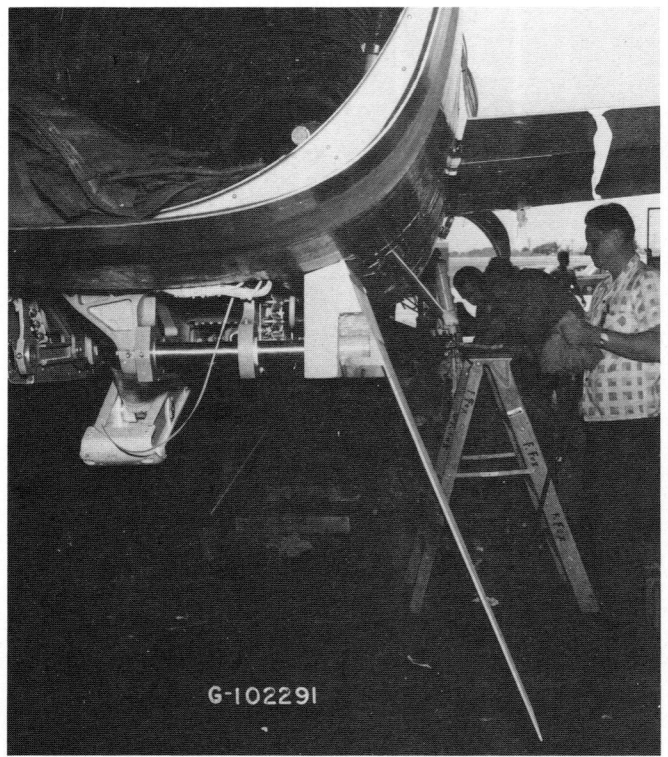

The ventral fins rotated to an "up" position to provide clearance when the aircraft was on the ground. At left, the fin is shown in its "in-flight" position, while at right it is in the "up" position. The fins rotated at a pivot point located where the trailing edge connected to the aircraft. Thus, by rotating 180° around this pivot point, the fin was in the "up" position behind the stabilator, and, in this position, the trailing edge became the leading edge. No details of its use could be found in Grumman's files, and there is no indication that the aircraft flew with these fins in place.
(Grumman)

ROHR TIGERS

Tigers 141853 and 141824 were used in a test program to evaluate in-flight thrust control. This evaluation was conducted in 1973, after the F11F had been retired from service. Both aircraft were painted in beautiful paint schemes, and color photos are on the front cover and on page 40. Here, 141853, the aircraft to be fitted with the thrust reverser, is seen prior to the installation of the device. The other aircraft was used simply as a chase plane. **(Grumman)**

When the Blue Angels retired the Tiger in 1969, it seemed as though the flying days of the F11F (by now designated F11A) were over. But in 1973, two Tigers were used for a test program for the ROHR thrust reverser. One aircraft, 141853, was fitted with the reverser, and a second, 141824, was used as a chase plane. Unlike the "Super Tiger" program, this ROHR evaluation was not intended to improve or modify the Tiger in particular. Instead, the F11A was simply a suitable airframe for the ROHR thrust reverser. The tests were conducted to evaluate the reverser rather than the Tiger itself.

Charles "Chuck" Sewell flew the first flight with the reverser on February 9, 1973. After the tests, 141853 was placed in the Pima Air Museum, complete with the reverser still installed.

This photo shows 141853 after installation of the thrust reverser. **(Picciani)**

With the thrust reverser still installed, 141853 is seen at its final resting place, the Pima County Air Museum near Tucson, Arizona.

Left: Close-up of the special markings on the tail of 141853.

Below: Close-up of the thrust reverser showing details from the left rear.

ROHR TIGER COCKPIT

Instrument panel and control column in 141853.

Left console detail showing throttle quadrant.

View looking back at the top of the seat and the open canopy.

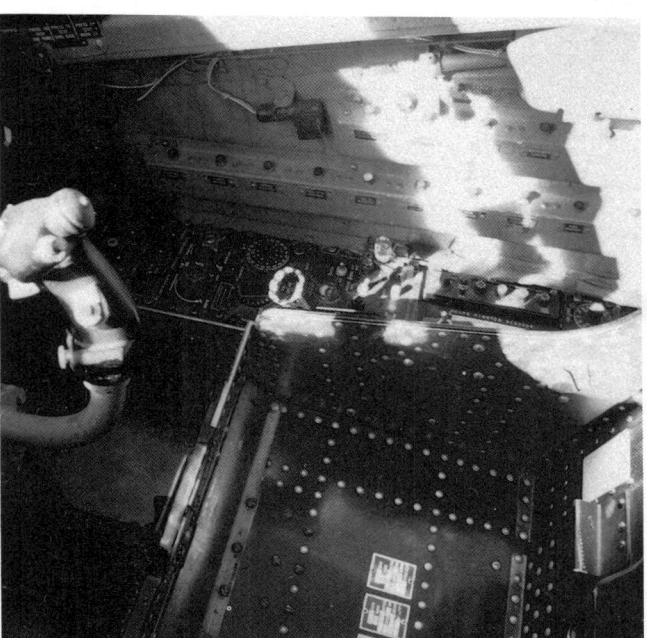

Right side of the cockpit showing control column and right console.

TIGER MARKINGS

F11F-1, 168618, is shown about to be hoisted on to the USS Saratoga. NATC is on the tail in black letters, and although it is hard to discern, the tail and nose are painted in high visibility orange. (Grumman)

NAVAL AIR TEST CENTER

Left: "Short nose" F11F-1, 138617, is shown here with a larger NATC on the tail and no high visibility markings. (Grumman)

Below: This "long nose" Tiger, 141729, bears the same NATC markings as 138618 above, except that the high visibility markings on the nose is a band behind the radome instead of extending to the tip of the nose. (U.S. Navy)

VX-3

The unit designation, VX-3, is painted above the word NAVY on both sides of the aircraft as evidenced by this photo of 138627. VX-3 received some of the first Tigers built.   (Grumman)

Right and left side views of 138652 on the catapult show more of VX-3's markings. The pilot's name was painted on both sides of the aircraft, just above the nose number. The aircraft is painted in the standard light gull gray over white scheme.   (Grumman)

VX-3 F11F-1, 138617, is shown being launched from the waist catapult of the USS Saratoga. The aircraft number is on the nose and tail, and the last four digits of the BuNo are also on the tail. All lettering is in black.   (Grumman)

VA-156 & VF-111

VA-156 was the first operational Navy squadron to receive the F11F-1. Originally they were equipped with "short nose" Tigers as seen here. *(National Archives)*

Later, VA-156 converted to "long nose" Tigers, but the markings remained the same as evidenced by this photo of 110 doing a touch-and-go landing aboard an Essex class carrier. *(National Archives)*

Before transitioning out of F11F-1s, VA-156 was redesignated VF-111, and used these simple markings. Note the anti-glare panel on the second aircraft from the top. At the time this photo was taken, VF-111 was operating from the USS Shangri La, CVA-38, and was part of Carrier Air Group Eleven. This photo was taken over Japan. *(U.S. Navy)*

VF-191

VF-191 was another Pacific coast squadron that operated the Tiger. The only distinctive markings are the NM on the tail and the VF-191 under the NAVY on each side of the fuselage. **(Picciani)**

Two VF-191 Tigers extend their tail hooks in preparation for landing. No special markings or designs were carried on VF-191 aircraft. **(Grumman)**

VF-121

VF-121 flew "long nose" Tigers that had a red flash on the nose. The broad tail band is red with black inner stripes and red outer stripes.   (U.S. Navy)

A VF-121 Tiger is ready for launch from the USS Lexington, CVA-16.   (U.S. Navy)

Another VF-121 Tiger has been brought to a stop during operations aboard the Lexington.   (U.S. Navy)

VF-211

VF-211, formerly designated VF-51 and VF-24, flew the Tiger in the Pacific. Here a VF-211 aircraft is about to be launched. Again, the carrier is the USS Lexington. (U.S. Navy)

Two VF-211 Tigers are seen over Mt. Fuji. (U.S. Navy)

A deck crewman scrambles clear after disengaging the arresting cable from the tail hook of this F11F-1 from VF-211. (U.S. Navy)

VF-33

Atlantic coast squadron, VF-33, marked its Tigers with yellow lightning bolts. The squadron insignia appears on the fuselage above the wing.

(Grumman)

Another VF-33 Tiger is shown on the Intrepid in front of a row of A-4 Skyhawks from VA-66 and VA-76. Note the black anti-glare panel and the fact that the entire BuNo is on the tail. Usually only the last four digits were painted on the tail.

(U.S. Navy)

VF-21

The other Atlantic coast squadron to fly the Tiger was VF-21. A yellow shark's mouth and yellow and black bands on the tail characterized the markings of this unit. When this photo was taken, the tail code was AD. Aircraft 201 is venting fuel from its wing vents.   (Grumman)

With the tail code now changed to AM, this VF-21 aircraft is ready for launch from the USS Forrestal.
(National Archives)

Another VF-21 F11F-1 has caught the wire after a successful landing. This view shows the wing markings to good effect.
(National Archives)

CARRIER OPERATIONS

F11F-1, 138618, is hoisted aboard the USS Forrestal for carrier trials. This view shows underside details to good effect.
(National Archives)

This interesting view of 138618 on an elevator shows braces on the folded part of the wing.
(National Archives)

The hook is down and this Tiger is about to catch the wire on the Forrestal.
(National Archives)

Tigers from NATC and VX-3 line up for launch. The launch signal has just been given for 138614 on the starboard "cat." (Grumman)

This head-on view shows the deck crewmen positioning a "short nose" Tiger on the port catapult of the USS Saratoga. (Grumman)

One of the Tigers assigned to the Naval Air Test Center gets a tow across the flight deck of the USS Saratoga. Note the lowered boarding steps. (Grumman)

Other "short nose" Tigers are shown on the Saratoga's flight deck. The aircraft on the left has the area rule fuel tanks and Sidewinders under the wings. "Short nose" Tigers primarily went to NATC, VX-3 and VA-156. Initially, the Blue Angels also flew the "short nose" version before changing over to the "long nose" aircraft. (Grumman)

F11F-1's from VF-33 are seen during flight operations aboard the USS Intrepid, CVA-11. This view shows the lightning bolt on the right wing tip to good effect. The word "Astronauts" has been added next to the squadron insignia.
(U.S. Navy)

Two VF-21 Tigers are being readied for launch from the Forrestal's port catapult while an A-4 Skyhawk is launched from one of the waist catapults.
(U.S. Navy)

One F11F-1 sits on the starboard "cat" on the USS Hancock, CVA-19, while another is taken down to the hanger deck on the forward elevator. Three F8U Crusaders are shown well forward on the deck.
(National Archives)

This unusual night shot is of a "short nose" F11F being launched from the Saratoga. The picture is a three minute time exposure.
(Grumman)

Number 207 from VF-33 lands aboard the Intrepid during "Operation Big Deal," February 27, 1959.(U.S. Navy)

A crewman rushes to the tail of F11F-1, 141855, to free the tail hook from the arresting gear after a landing aboard the USS Lexington. This photo was taken on March 19, 1959. (U.S. Navy)

F11F-1, 138728, from the Flight Test Division of NATC, Pax River, Maryland, makes a touch-and-go landing on the angled deck of the USS Forrestal, CVA-59, during "Operation Crosswind."

(U.S. Navy)

An NATC Tiger approaches the fantail with gear down, flaps down, and hook down. Note the extension of the main gear oleo struts with the aircraft in the air. (Grumman)

MODELER'S SECTION

KIT REVIEWS

1/100th SCALE KIT

MONOGRAM 1/100th SCALE F11F-1 BLUE ANGELS SET

This is a set of "short nose" Tigers released by Monogram around 1959. The set is designed to be built as an in-flight display of Blue Angels aircraft, and is really quite attractive. Markings are for the Blue Angels' "short nose" scheme which was different from that used on the "long nose" Tigers flown later by the team.

Scaling out the dimensions reveals that the scale is closer to 1/102nd scale, but the model fits nicely in a 1/100th scale collection. Construction is quite simple with only a few parts to assemble. The wings, horizontal tails, and upper fuselage are all molded together as one piece. The vertical tail fits into a slot on the top of this piece, and the lower fuselage half fits under it. With this done, all that is left is for the modeler to add the pilot and seat, which are molded together as one piece, then cover the cockpit with the single-piece canopy. This completes the model as it comes in the box. Since the kit builds into an in-flight set, there is no landing gear provided.

Surface scribing is recessed and nicely done. It does include some of the decal locations as was often the case with kits issued in the 1950's. If a scheme other than that used for the Blue Angels is used, these decal location lines should be filled in and sanded out. Molding is nicely done with very little flash in evidence. However, a flaw in the molding was present on the trailing edge of the right wing tip on our models. This can easily be removed with a little sanding and rescribing of the wing tip panel line.

The model is hollow, having that "look in the intake, see out the exhaust" problem. A tailpipe should be fashioned from a tube that is plugged at one end. Once inserted in the model, this will make the model look much more realistic. Another addition that would be worthwhile is to use plastic stock to make

The smallest scale Tiger is this model from Monogram. It was part of a Blue Angel team display.

walls for inside the intakes. Combined with the added tailpipe, this will eliminate the hollow look of the model.

For modelers interested in a 1/100th scale collection, this model could be an even nicer addition if landing gear was added. Since the Tiger is such a small aircraft, we suggest using landing gear parts from 1/144th scale kits. First, the openings for the wheel wells should be cut out, and plastic card can be used to wall in the insides of the wells. The nose gear doors can be made from plastic card, as can the small doors that are attached to the rear struts on the main gear. The larger upper doors for the main gear will require some curvature, and this can be achieved by vacuforming plastic stock, then cutting it to the appropriate shape. With this work done, the model will look as nice as any of the present day 1/100th scale kits.

Although no longer available and rather hard to find, this is a very good little kit. We do hope Monogram will reissue it in their Heritage Edition kits. We recommend this kit.

1/72nd SCALE KITS

The Minicraft/Hasegawa F11F Tiger in 1/72nd scale is an excellent kit, and the best available of the Tiger.

MINICRAFT/HASEGAWA 1/72nd SCALE F11F

This kit is the most recently released of the F11F, and it is clearly the best available in any scale. It represents a "long nose" Tiger of the second production batch. Movable control surfaces are represented with recessed lines, while other panel lines are the raised type. Detailing is nicely done and quite accurate. Dimensions and proportions are also correct.

The cockpit consists of a "tub," which includes the floor, sides, and consoles. An instrument panel, seat, and control column are also provided. Detailing the cockpit is left to decals for the instrument panel and consoles. This is sufficient for many modelers building in 1/72nd scale, but others may want to do further detailing. A throttle and seat belts would be the minimum recommended. This extra detailing would be even more important if the two-piece canopy is assembled in the open position.

Landing gear, tail hook, bumper skid, and ammunition chutes are all nicely done, being crisply molded and accurately detailed. Intakes and splitter plates are separate pieces that fit together, then attached to the fuselage sides. This prevents the hollow look that occurs when there is no inner wall to the intakes. If you look down into the intakes, a plug is visible. It is far enough inside the model that it is not usually visible, but a more realistic look can be achieved if this is removed before the intake is glued in place.

The wings and horizontal stabilizers are single-piece parts with no top/bottom combinations to worry about. Care should be taken to insure proper alignment when attaching these parts. Four pylons are provided for Sidewinder missiles to go under the wing. Two pylons with external tanks can be substituted for the two inboard pylons with the Sidewind-

ers. The pylons for the Sidewinders do not have the appropriate launch rail. This rail fits on the pylon, and the Sidewinder attaches to the rail rather than directly on the pylon as the kit has it. These rails can easily be added from plastic card. In building our sample model, we cut the rails from the pylons of a Minicraft F9F-8 Cougar kit, and glued them to the pylons. The Sidewinder missiles were then glued to the rails.

Fit is very good, and the model goes together quickly and easily. The model is finished before you know it, and is ready for any of a number of colorful schemes carried by the Tiger. It makes an excellent and important addition to any collection of naval fighters, and we recommend this kit as the best available of the Tiger.

AIRMODEL 1/72nd SCALE VACUFORMED F11F

Prior to the release of the Minicraft/Hasegawa injection molded kit, this vacuformed kit was the only 1/72nd scale Tiger that was available. It is now very hard to find, and not really worth the effort since the Minicraft kit builds into such a nice model. Its value lies only with collectors. Although we studied this kit several years ago, a sample was no longer available for use in a review in this publication.

OFF-SCALE KIT

REVELL 1/54th SCALE "SHORT NOSE" TIGER

This kit, originally copyrighted in 1956, is typical of Revell kits of the fifties, and has been released a number of times in different markings. We got out our original issue of this kit and built it for review here. As with most kits from the fifties, the locations for the decals are scribed in the plastic, and this original release comes with the swivel stand that was a trademark of Revell in those earlier days of plastic kits.

The model represents a "short nose" Tiger, complete with refueling receptacle on the nose. The receptacle is very poorly done, lacking any detail at all, and it is best cut off and replaced with a better one. We recommend cutting the receptacle off the end of a refueling probe from a 1/48th scale A-4 kit and using it instead. It won't be exactly right, but it will be a lot better than what comes in the kit. The landing gear is very crude, and does not even approach any degree of accuracy. There isn't much that can be done to improve it, so we built our sample in the gear-up, in-flight configuration. Once the gear doors are glued in place, they can be sanded smooth to blend into the fuselage. Following this, they should be rescribed,

The off-scale "short nose" Tiger from Revell is typical of kits from the '50s, and has some serious problems.

but care must be taken to correct the shape of the nose gear doors. They are too short, and the leading edges are straight, rather than being pointed as they should be. Check the drawings in this book for the proper shape.

The fit of most of the parts is very poor, particularly for the horizontal stabilizers. Much filling and sanding is required. The wing tips can be positioned in the extended or folded position, but since we built our model in the in-flight configuration, this choice became academic. The tail pipe is plugged, and is round rather than being flattened on the bottom. We added a tail pipe that extended well into the rear of the fuselage, and corrected the shape as much as possible.

The cockpit is simply a hole that is filled with a piece that includes pilot, seat, and control column. We added an instrument panel and consoles, but they are barely visible once the canopy is glued in place.

The shape and proportions are adequate, not being really accurate, but not so far off either. It is good enough for a desk model, but not for an accurate scale replica.

In short, it is best to keep the vintage of this kit in mind. It is almost thirty years old, and, unlike wine, models do not improve with age. Building such a kit can be a nostalgic trip into the past for modelers who are old enough to remember when such kits were first released. The resulting model can be a real conversation piece and an interesting addition to any collection.

1/48th SCALE KIT
LINDBERG 1/48th SCALE PROTOTYPE TIGER

This kit is supposedly in 1/48th scale, but actual measurements show it to be off of that standard scale a bit. Each measurement works out to a different scale when compared to the real thing. The best that can be said is that it is in the "ball park" of 1/48th scale. It represents a prototype aircraft with the very short nose of 138604, but also has the intake splitter and gun fairings which were added later. It would appear that the model is a hybrid, representing both 138604 and 138606.

The kit is really more of a toy than a scale model, and comes with movable control surfaces and a door that opens on the right side of the fuselage to reveal the engine. The real aircraft had no such door.

The forward speed brake is of the rectangular type, with perforations scribed in. The aft brakes are not even scribed in the plastic. The landing gear is not remotely accurate, so if this kit is built at all, a gear-up in-flight model is the only real choice possible. There is a refueling receptacle which is better than the one in the Revell kit, but it would be better to replace it with an instrumentation probe. This is because the kit can only be built as a prototype aircraft, and the actual prototypes usually had such probes.

Surface scribing is a combination of raised and recessed lines with hundreds of rivets. It is best to sand all of these off, leaving a basic desk stand model which merely provides the shape of the aircraft. What details are scribed in are wrong, so it doesn't hurt to sand them off. Even the air intake slots, located on the sides of the fuselage just above the trailing edge of the wing roots, are too far down on the fuselage, and this would be most difficult to correct. The wing fences are also wrong, being flat on top rather than curved.

The cockpit has a two-piece seat, pilot, instrument panel, and control column. None of this is very accurate, but, considering the rest of the model, it really isn't worth correcting. External stores include eight 5-inch rockets to go under the wings, but these are inaccurate for the F11F, so they should not be used.

The kit was not available for some time, but was re-released a few years ago by Hobby Net Work. Two kits were issued, one with Blue Angels' markings, and one with markings for VX-3 and VF-21. Since this model represents an early prototype, and none of these units ever flew such an aircraft, these markings are all inaccurate. Lindberg has also re-released the kit, and it also has Blue Angels' markings.

The only reason we can see why anyone would want to build this kit is if they simply had to have a model of a prototype Tiger. Granted, it is an old kit that dates back almost thirty years, but, even considering this, it simply is not accurate enough to justify building it as a serious scale model.

DECAL SUMMARY

Note: It is impossible to completely review decals unless the reviewer has actually used the decals on a model to see how they fit. Additionally, markings on a given aircraft can be changed from time to time, so it is possible that the decals may be accurate for one point in time and not another. Therefore, this section is more of a listing of decals available than a review. Review comments are made only in regard to fit when we have actually used the decals or as to accuracy when the evidence clearly indicated an error.

KIT DECALS

1/100th SCALE KIT

Monogram 1/100th Scale Blue Angels Kit: Provides markings for a set of Blue Angels' "short nose" Tigers.

1/72nd SCALE KIT

Minicraft/Hasegawa 1/72nd Scale F11F-1: Provides markings for two aircraft.
- F11F-1, 141740, VF-21, with tigershark mouth on nose. The nose number is 205, and the tail code is AD. The aircraft is painted in the gull gray over white scheme.
- F11F-1, 141872, of the Blue Angels. This is the leader's aircraft, and has a number 1 on the tail.

OFF-SCALE KIT

Revell 1/54th Scale "Short Nose" Tiger: The original release of this kit had ficticious markings for an aircraft with a BuNo of 279173. This is incorrect for any F11F. The insignia on the tail was a tiger jumping through a flaming hoop. A re-release of this kit in 1960 included Blue Angels' markings for the team's "short nose" Tigers.

1/48th SCALE KIT

Lindberg 1/48th Scale Prototype Tiger: As most recently released, this kit provides markings for a Blue Angels' aircraft. One release by Hobby Net Work also provides markings for the Blue Angels. A second Hobby Net Work release provides markings for VX-3 and VF-21. In all cases, the markings are inaccurate for the prototype aircraft represented by the kit.

DECAL SHEETS

1/72nd SCALE SHEETS

Microscale Sheet Number 72-255: Provides markings for four aircraft, all in the gull gray over white scheme.
- F11F-1, 141745, VA-156, CVG-11, USS Shangri-La, 1956. The nose number is 110, and the tail code is NH.
- F11F-1, 141825, VF-51, "Screaming Eagles," CVW-5, USS Ranger, 1958. The nose number is 105, and the tail code is NF.
- F11F-1, 141777, VF-121. The nose number is 101, and the tail code is NJ.
- F11F-1, 141771, VF-33, "Astronauts." The nose number is 206, and the tail code is AF.

Scale-Master Sheet SM-19: Provides markings for one F11F-1, 141783, VF-33 "Astronauts." The nose number is 210, and the tail code is AF.

Note: The yellow used on this sheet is too pale. A darker yellow should have been used in printing these decals.

Scale-Master Sheet SM-22: Provides markings for three aircraft.
- F11F-1, 141857, VF-121. The nose number is 115, and the tail code is NJ.
- F11F-1, 141730, VA-156. The nose number is 103, and the tail code is NH.
- F11F-1, 141785, VF-191. The nose number is 105, and the tail code is NM.

Notes: The red used on this sheet is thin, and we recommend painting the areas white that these red decals will cover before applying the decals. This is not necessary on the nose marking on 141857. On 141857, the red band on the tail is bordered by two stripes on both the top and bottom edges. The decal sheet has all of these stripes red, when the inner stripe in both cases should be black.